TOTAL HEALTH

TALKING ABOUT LIFE'S CHANGES

STUDENT WORKBOOK

SUSAN BOE

purposeful design
publications
A Division of ACSI

Colorado Springs, Colorado

Purposeful Design Publications is the publishing division of the Association of Christian Schools International (ACSI) and is committed to the ministry of Christian school education, to enable Christian educators and schools worldwide to effectively prepare students for life. As the publisher of textbooks, trade books, and other educational resources within ACSI, Purposeful Design Publications strives to produce biblically sound materials that reflect Christian scholarship and stewardship and that address the identified needs of Christian schools around the world.

Printed in the United States of America
25 24 23 22 21 20 19 18 17 16   9 10 11 12 13 14 15 16 17 18 19 20

Boe, Susan
   Talking about life's changes: Student workbook
   Second edition
   Total Health series
   ISBN 978-1-58331-232-2   Test and quiz master book   Catalog #7600

Cover design: Sarah E. Schultz

Purposeful Design Publications
A Division of ACSI
PO Box 65130 • Colorado Springs, CO 80962-5130
Customer Service: 800/367-0798 • Website: www.acsi.org

Table of Contents
Student Workbook

Name _____   Date _____

Vocabulary

Match the seven words below with the corresponding letter from the list at the bottom of the page.

Deception _____

Temptation _____

Consequences _____

Habits _____

Soul _____

Influences _____

Total Health _____

a. a repetitious pattern of behavior

b. an attraction to something, often harmful

c. the power to produce change through people or situations

d. the outcome or result

e. misleading deliberately

f. the all-encompassing well-being of a person

g. the mind, will and emotions

Name _____   Date _____

The Two Trees

In the space provided, list the thoughts, actions, and attitudes that represent each tree.

TREE OF LIFE   **TREE OF DEATH**

How can a person successfully win this daily conflict between these two trees?

Name _____ Date _____

Keeping Track of My Daily Influences

From the list provided, make a chart within the circle based on the estimated average amount of time you spend with the following influences during one week. The chart is based on 15 hour days, giving you nine hours spent in bed sleeping each night. Total hours awake for the week (average) 105.

Color the spaces in your week's pie as indicated by subject.

❏   (green) The time I spend watching Television:

❏   (dark blue) The time I spend at school: (7hrs a day 5 days/week =35 hrs week)

❏   (yellow) The time I spend listening to music:

❏   (dark brown) The time I spend reading:

❏   (light brown) The time I spend reading magazines and/or comic books:

❏   (red) The time I spend hanging out with my friends:

❏   (orange) The time I spend at church/youth group activities:

❏   (orange) The time I spend reading my Bible:

❏   (orange) The time I spend having personal quiet time with God:

❏   (light blue) The time I spend with my family:

Conclusion

What activities take up the most of your time? Are these positive or negative influences? What areas would you like to spend more time with? Less time with? How can a teenager keep track of his/her influences?

Name _____   Date _____

"Me, Glorify God?"
YES!

BIBLE STUDY

1. Who is the greatest hero in your life?

   Who is your favorite actor or actress?

   When you get emotionally excited about your favorite hero or favorite star, tell others about them, and go to see their movies as much as you can, you're really "glorifying" them. Look up the words "*glory*" and "*glorify*" and in the dictionary. How do you think that these definitions apply to God?

2. Read *John* 16:14. When a person is born again, God sends His Holy Spirit to live inside of them. What does the Spirit do in and through Christians' lives? (It's something that increases more and more all the time throughout a Christian's entire life.)

3. Look up *Psalm* 50:23 and *Matthew* 5:16. In the first verse, in what two ways do we glorify God? In the second, in what way do we as Christians bring honor to God? Is verbally praising and thanking God enough to really be "glorifying" God?

4. Jesus said, "By this My Father is glorified, that you bear much fruit..." (*John* 15:8) What do you think that He meant by "bear much fruit"? How does that bring praise to God?

(cont. ➤➤)

5. Do you think that Christians can glorify God even in the "negative" experiences of their lives? Read the following verses and list the two "negative" or painful experiences in which Christians can bring praise to God.

• *John* 21:19, Christians can glorify God in their...

• *I Peter* 4:16, Christians do glorify God when they...

6. Read *I Corinthians* 6:20. In what two areas of our lives does Paul say to "glorify" God? What do you think Paul means by glorifying God in these two areas of our lives?

7. When Jesus said, "And I do not seek My own glory..." (*John* 8:50), what do you think that He meant? How do you think that *Revelation* 18:7 would contrast with that?

8. Read *Jeremiah* 9:23,24. In what three areas did the prophet say people should not be proud and arrogant? How do you think this applies to the American culture or to your life?

(cont. ➡)

Name _____   Date _____

"Me, Glorify God?"
YES! (cont.)

9. Concerning *Jeremiah* 9:23,24: in what four things does God delight (because they give Him glory)? Give one example of how each of these points applies to your life.

   1.)

   Example:

   2.)

   Example:

   3.)

   Example:

   4.)

   Example:

10. God wants to glorify Himself through you! After doing this Bible study, in what areas of your life do you want to "glorify" God more?

Name _____   Date _____

God's Promises to Me

BIBLE STUDY

"By which have been given to us exceedingly great and precious promises, that through these you may be partakers of the divine nature."
II Peter 1:4

Look up the following verses, then match the most appropriate promise with each verse. (There may be more than one verse for some promises.)

_____ *James* 1:5

_____ *Psalm* 147:3

_____ *Philippians* 4:19

_____ *Psalm* 141:3

_____ *Jeremiah* 29:11

_____ *Psalm* 51:2

_____ *II Timothy* 1:7

_____ *Psalm* 29:11

_____ *Matthew* 11:28

_____ *Psalm* 23:4

_____ *I Corinthians* 10:13

_____ *Psalm* 32:8

_____ *Isaiah* 41:10

_____ *Psalm* 147:5

_____ *Proverbs* 3:6

_____ *Philippians* 4:7

_____ *Psalm* 27:1

_____ *Romans* 8:37

A. God will direct and lead my life.

B. God will take care of my future.

C. God will heal my broken heart.

D. God will forgive my sins.

E. God will give me strength when I am tempted.

F. God will help me not to gossip.

G. God will help me when I am afraid.

H. God will comfort me when no one understands me.

I. God will take care of all of my needs.

J. God will comfort me when I am lonely.

K. God will give me wisdom when I ask.

L. God will give me peace when I am stressed-out.

M. God will help me when I am tired.

Name _____   Date _____

Vocabulary

Match the circulatory related terms from the list below with the definitions and put the correct letter in the blank after each definition.

1. The component in the blood that fights germs, viruses and diseases _____

2. The smallest blood vessels found in the body _____

3. A disease which involves hardening of the arteries _____

4. The component of the blood responsible for carrying oxygen _____

5. A severe restriction of blood flow to part of the brain _____

6. The portion of the blood that causes clotting _____

7. The force placed against the inside walls of your blood vessels _____

8. Blood vessels that carry oxygen-depleted blood back to the heart _____

9. The liquid portion of the blood _____

10. Blood vessels that carry oxygenated blood away from the heart _____

a. arteriosclerosis

b. plasma

c. red blood cells

d. capillaries

e. platelets

f. blood pressure

g. stroke

h. arteries

i. veins

j. white blood cells

Part Two

Circle the correct answer of those given after each definition.

1. The _____ cleanse the blood of impurities and send it back to the bloodstream. (Pharynx, small intestine, kidneys)

2. A balanced, stable environment within the body would be called _____. (stroke, hormones, homeostasis)

3. The long muscular tube which includes many digestive functions and runs throughout the body is the _____. (alimentary canal, esophagus, diaphragm)

4. The small flap of skin that prevents food from entering the trachea is the _____. (diaphragm, epiglottis, pharynx)

(cont. ➤➤)

5. The process of breaking down food and making it usable for the body is called ____. (digestion, homeostasis, arteriosclerosis)

6. The portion of the digestive tract responsible for waste functions is the ____. (esophagus, small intestine, large intestine)

7. A passageway that carries air to the lungs is called the ____. (epiglottis, trachea, diaphragm)

8. The heart muscle could also be called the ____. (smooth muscle, skeletal muscle, cardiac muscle)

9. The basic building blocks of the body are called ____. (veins, cells, capillaries)

10. The ____ is often referred to as the throat. (pharynx, epiglottis, trachea)

11. The ____ release hormones when we are under certain types of stress. (kidneys, cells, adrenal glands)

12. Most digestion and absorption of nutrients takes place in the ____. (small intestine, large intestine, alimentary canal)

13. "Chemical messengers" released by the glands of the endocrine system. ____ (platelets, hormones, plasma)

14. If an individual is experiencing a state of physical, mental, social and spiritual well being that person can be said to be ____. (healthy, tissues, homeostasis)

15. Similar cells organized into specialized groups to carry out particular functions could be called ____. (platelets, hormones, tissues)

16. An ____ exists when two or more tissues are grouped together to perform a particular function. (alimentary canal, organ, ovaries)

17. The passageway responsible for carrying food to the stomach is the ____. (epiglottis, small intestine, esophagus)

18. The rate at which the body metabolizes food is controlled by hormones released from the ____. (testes, ovaries, thyroid gland)

19. The glands of the female reproductive system responsible for female sex characteristics are the ____. (testes, pituitary gland, ovaries)

20. Muscles found in the digestive system and blood vessels are referred to as ____.(cardiac muscles, platelets, smooth muscles)

21. The glands responsible for male sex characteristics are called the ____. (kidneys, testes, ovaries)

22. Human growth hormone is released by the ____. (testes, thyroid gland, pituitary gland)

23. The ____ are the principle organs of the respiratory system. (lungs, kidneys, adrenal glands)

24. Muscles responsible for the movements of the body are the ____. (smooth muscles, cardiac muscles, skeletal muscles)

25. The chest and abdomen are separated by a muscle wall called the ____. (epiglottis, diaphragm, trachea)

Name _____   Date _____

The Life of a Cell

Color the picture of the cell and list the eight common characteristics of every cell. What is meant by the phrase, "Good health begins at the cellular level"? How might this phrase relate to poor health as well?

1. _____   2. _____

8. _____   3. _____

7. _____   4. _____

6. _____   5. _____

Name _____   Date _____

The Flow of Blood Through the Heart

For the numbers within the heart, place arrows in the appropriate direction to show correct blood flow. For the numbers outside the heart, describe what activity is occurring corresponding to the number in the heart.

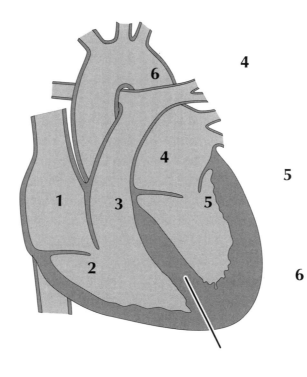

Name _____   Date _____

The Circulatory System

Label the appropriate veins and arteries. Write a brief paragraph on the benefits of having a healthy circulatory system. You may use the back of this worksheet.

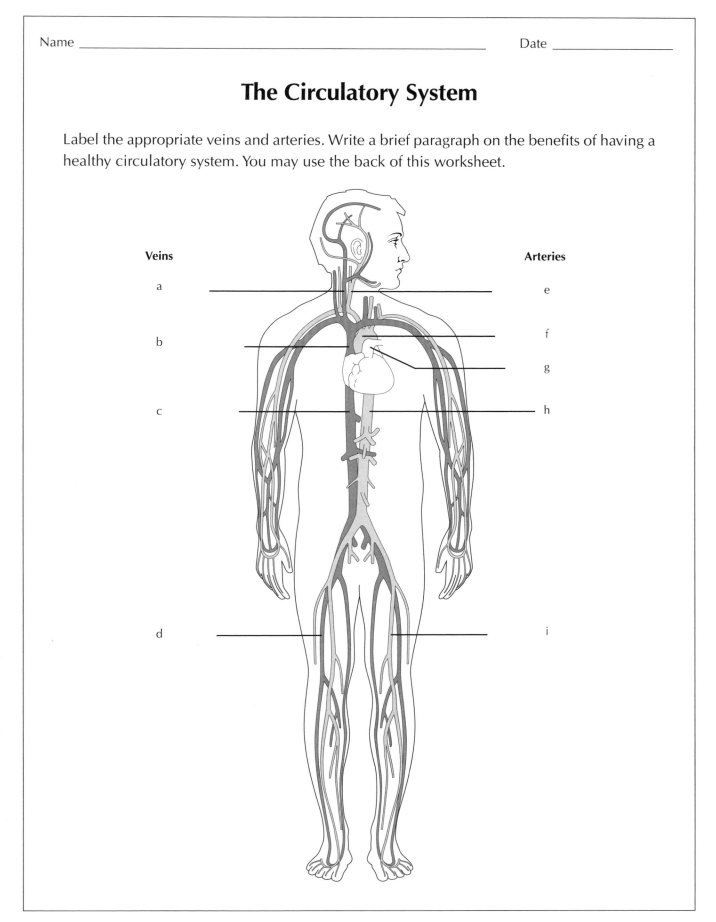

Veins

a

b

c

d

Arteries

e

f

g

h

i

Name _____ Date _____

The Respiratory System

Label the correct parts of the respiratory system. Write a brief paragraph explaining how a person can properly care for his/her reaspiratory system. You may use the back of this worksheet.

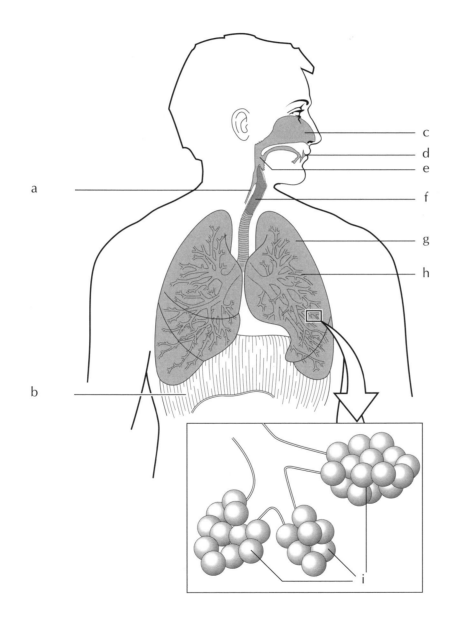

Name _____   Date _____

The Skeletal System

Label the appropriate parts of the skeletal system. Using the back of this worksheet, write a brief paragraph describing the four types of bones in the body.

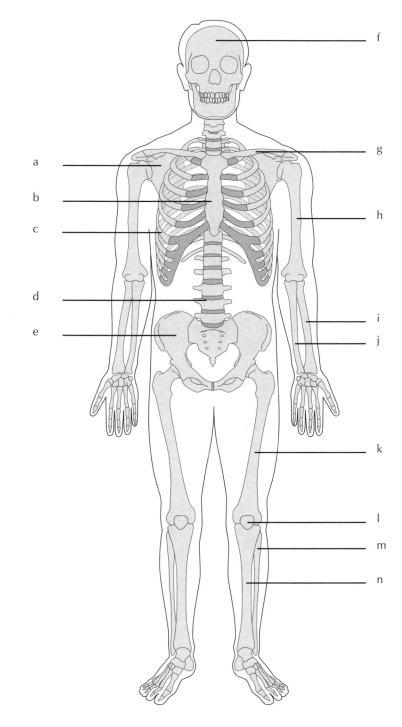

Name _____   Date _____

The Muscular System

Label the parts of the muscular system, and on the back of this worksheet write a brief paragraph on the benefits of exercise to the muscular system.

Posterior/Back Muscles

a _____

b _____

c _____

d _____

e _____

f _____

Anterior/Front Muscles

g _____

h _____

i _____

j _____

k _____

l _____

m _____

Name _____ Date _____

The Digestive and Excretory Systems

Label the parts of the digestive and excretory systems. Using the back of this worksheet, write a brief paragraph on the benefits of having healthy digestive and excretory systems.

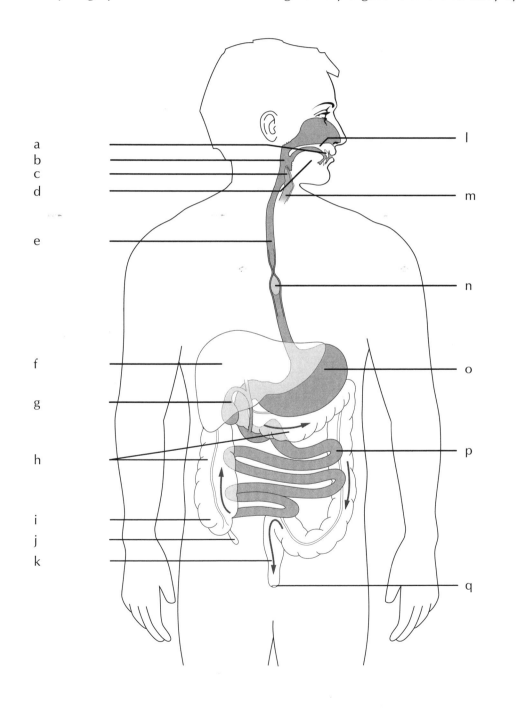

a
b
c
d

e

f

g

h

i
j
k

l

m

n

o

p

q

Name _____   Date _____

The Endocrine System

Label the appropriate parts of the male and female endocrine systems.

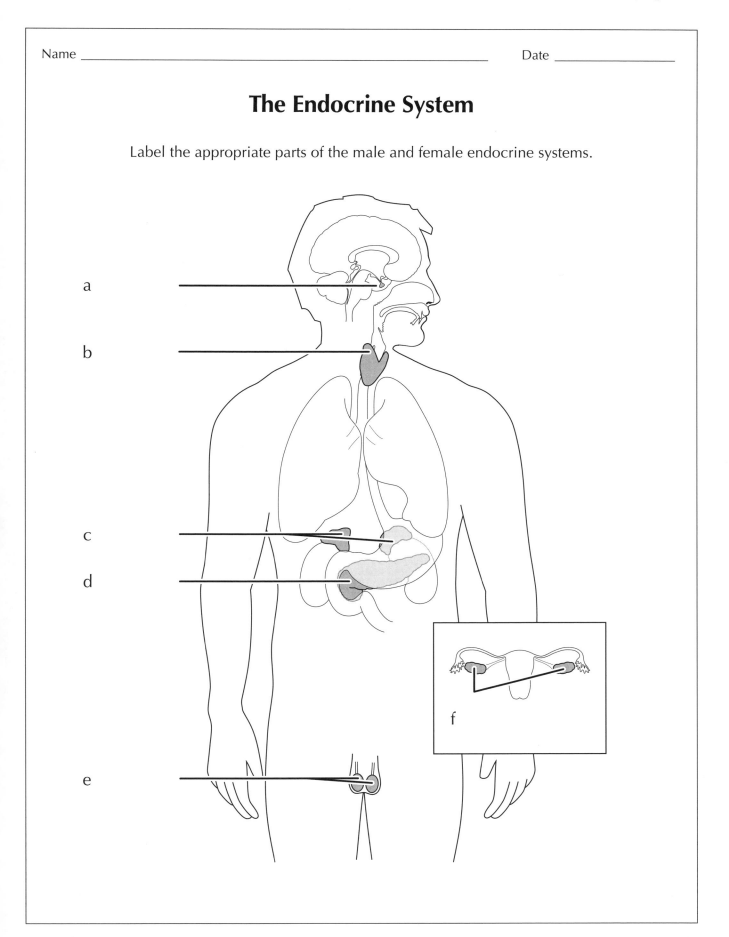

a

b

c

d

e

f

Name _____   Date _____

Vocabulary

Define the following terms:

1. Balanced diet:

2. Empty calorie:

3. Proteins:

4. Carbohydrates:

5. Fats:

6. RDA:

7. Anorexia:

8. Bulimia:

9. Chronic overeating:

10. Metabolic rate:

11. Vegetarian diet:

12. Diet:

(cont. ➤➤)

Part Two

Write the word in the blank that fits best. Choose your words from the list below.

1. When Roger realized he was over 20% beyond his ideal body weight he knew he had become _____ and needed to make some changes to reverse the problem.

2. It was recommended that I take a supplement to insure I get a proper balance of _____ and _____.

3. Our energy use and needs are measured in heat units called _____.

4. To minimize the risk of heart disease doctors can monitor the levels of _____ in our blood and make recommendations to lower the concentration should it become too high.

5. The _____ in the foods we eat insure that we receive needed supplies of vitamins, minerals and fuel for energy and restoration.

6. Some vitamins pass through the system easily and are not stored and so are called _____.

7. Other vitamins can be stored in the body and can even cause harm should the concentrations become too high. These substances are _____.

8. _____ are a group of eight substances your body needs for growth and maintenance that it does not produce on its own and must be contained in the foods you eat.

9. I knew I was heavier than recommended for my age, sex and size and so faced the fact that I had slowly become _____.

10. The fatty substances less likely to raise blood cholesterol levels are _____.

11. The bacon grease that congeals in the bottom of the frying pan, and one of many substances that will contribute to an increased cholesterol level in the blood is a graphic example of a _____.

Nutrients	Unsaturated fats
Overweight	Cholesterol
Minerals	Fat soluble
Essential amino acids	Vitamins
Water soluble	Saturated fat
Obese	Calories

Name _____   Date _____

Counting Calories

Keep track of the calories you consume for one day.

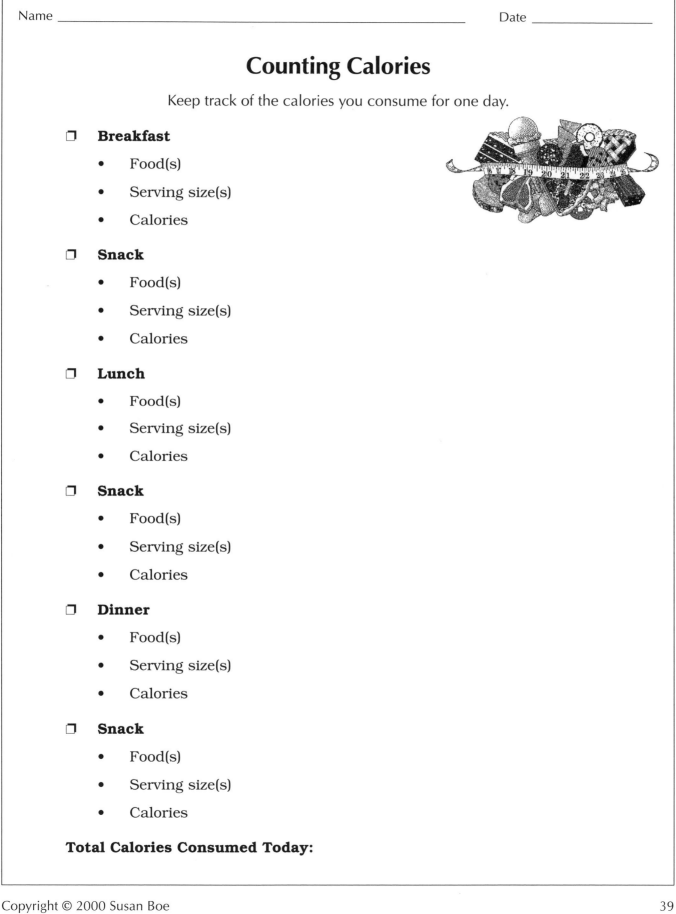

- ❏ **Breakfast**
    - Food(s)
    - Serving size(s)
    - Calories

- ❏ **Snack**
    - Food(s)
    - Serving size(s)
    - Calories

- ❏ **Lunch**
    - Food(s)
    - Serving size(s)
    - Calories

- ❏ **Snack**
    - Food(s)
    - Serving size(s)
    - Calories

- ❏ **Dinner**
    - Food(s)
    - Serving size(s)
    - Calories

- ❏ **Snack**
    - Food(s)
    - Serving size(s)
    - Calories

Total Calories Consumed Today:

Name _____ Date _____

Are You a Vegetarian?

There are many variations to a vegetarian diet. Do a report on the different kinds of meatless diets. Include reasons why people choose a vegetarian diet, the benefits associated with it, and the possible drawbacks.

1.

2.

3.

4.

Name _____   Date _____

The Great Pizza Potential

This worksheet can be done in conjunction with a classroom activity as described in the Teacher's Edition.

After selecting your pizza from the menu of a local pizza parlor, answer the following questions.

1.   The name of my pizza:

2.   The ingredients of my pizza:

3.   What is the source of protein in my pizza?

4.   What is the source of carbohydrate in my pizza?

5.   What is the source of fat in my pizza?

6.   What is the source of vitamins and/or minerals in my pizza?

7.   Use the numbers 1-10 to grade the nutritional value of your pizza (1 being very unhealthy and 10 being very healthy).

8.   The next time you order, what would you change to order a healthier pizza?

9.   How does your pizza taste?

10. Would you order this pizza again?

Name _____   Date _____

Where's the Beef?

Go to your local grocery store's health food section of the frozen foods. Write down the product names, ingredients, and cost for the vegetarian (meatless) burgers that you find. If you find meatless hotdogs, add them to your list as well. If you are up for the challenge, try a meatless burger like a Garden Burger™ and write your opinion on its taste and quality.

Product Name:

Ingredients:

Cost:

Product Name:

Ingredients:

Cost:

Product Name:

Ingredients:

Cost:

Have you ever eaten a meatless burger such as a Garden Burger™?   Yes ❏   No ❏

If yes, what is your opinion of the taste and quality?

Would you eat a meatless burger again?   Yes ❏   No ❏

Why or why not?

Name _____ Date _____

What's the Fuss over Bottled Water?

The human body is composed of approximately 70% water. There is a growing concern about the safety of today's drinking water. Go to your local grocery store and write down every type and brand of bottled water you find including the cost of each brand. Why do you think people spend money on water when it is free to drink out of their own tap? What do you think is the difference between tap water and bottled water?

The Name of the Bottled Water and Cost:

1. Name:

    Claim (or ingredients):

    Price:

2. Name:

    Claim (or ingredients):

    Price:

3. Name:

    Claim (or ingredients):

    Price:

4. What is Distilled Water?

5. What is Mineral Water?

6. What is the difference between hard versus soft water?

7. Do you drink bottled water? If yes, why? What is your favorite bottled water and why?

Name _____   Date _____

What is Best?

At your local supermarket, compare the labels of frozen, canned and fresh vegetables. Choose two vegetables to compare. For example, frozen peas, canned peas, and fresh peas, or frozen corn, canned corn, fresh corn. You will only have a label for the packaged products—why is that? If you have any questions concerning the shelf life of a fresh product, ask the produce person in that store.

1. Name of Vegetable: _____

    Frozen
    Ingedients:

    Label information:

    Shelf life:

    Canned
    Ingedients:

    Label information

    Shelf life:

    Fresh
    Ingredients

    Shelf-life

2. Name of Vegetable: _____

    Frozen
    Ingedients:

    Label information:

    Shelf life:

    Canned
    Ingedients:

    Label information

    Shelf life:

    Fresh
    Ingredients:

    Shelf-life:

Conclusion: What I found to be the best nutritionally for me, and what we eat most in our home:

Name _____   Date _____

Sugar & Sugar Substitutes

Look through the food and drink products you have in your home. List five products that contain any of the following in their ingredients list: Sugars such as white and/or brown sugar, corn syrup, glucose, sucrose, dextrose, and fructose. Sugar substitutes such as saccharine, Nutrasweet™, and aspartame™. Then answer questions A, B, and C.

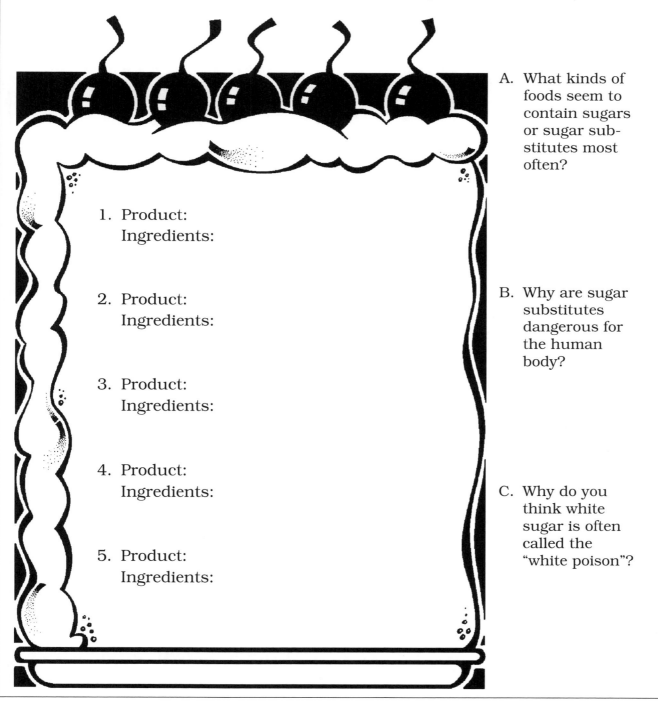

1. Product:
   Ingredients:

2. Product:
   Ingredients:

3. Product:
   Ingredients:

4. Product:
   Ingredients:

5. Product:
   Ingredients:

A. What kinds of foods seem to contain sugars or sugar substitutes most often?

B. Why are sugar substitutes dangerous for the human body?

C. Why do you think white sugar is often called the "white poison"?

Name _____   Date _____

The Dieting Industry
Your Money and Your Health

Go to your local drug store or diet aid section of your supermarket. Make a list of three diet aids you find, including their prices and claims. Include how long you are to take the product and any potential side effects or cautions listed.

1. Product:

   Cost:

   Claims:

   How long must I take this?

   What side effects might I experience?

   What cautions are listed?

2. Product:

   Cost:

   Claims:

   How long must I take this?

   What side effects might I experience?

   What cautions are listed?

3. Product:

   Cost:

   Claims:

   How long must I take this?

   What side effects might I experience?

   What cautions are listed?

Vocabulary

Crossword

ACROSS

2. The relationship between your fat and lean muscle body weight (two words)

6. The condition of your heart, lungs, and blood vessels to provide oxygenated blood to your whole body (two words)

DOWN

1. The power of your mind and body to work together to their highest possible level

3. Your muscles' strength and endurance (two words)

4. Short bursts of physical energy without the use of much oxygen, e.g., sprinting, golf, weight training

5. Physical activities you can do for as long as you are able, e.g., tennis, golf (two words)

7. Decrease in size and strength of muscles

8. When your muscles demand more oxygen than normal

10. The ability to move your joints and muscles through a full range of motion

Name _____   Date _____

Why Exercise Will Benefit Me

Write a paragraph explaining why exercise would be beneficial for you personally. Use the list from the Benefits of Exercise and apply specific reasons to what you are facing right now in your life. If you do not already have some form of exercise as a regular part of your life, explain why not.

Name _____   Date _____

Get The Beat

This activity will take you about 10 minutes to do. Try to do this at approximately the same time every day for one week. You may need someone to help you time yourself.

Taking your pulse: Place your two fingers (pointer and middle finger) on the side of your neck. You will feel your pulse on your carotid artery. Count your pulse for 10 seconds and multiply by 6. This will give you your heart rate per minute.

Instructions	**Day 1**	**Day 2**	**Day 3**	**Day 4**	**Day 5**	**Day 6**	**Day 7**
Measure your heart rate while sitting quietly.							
Do jumping jacks for 30 seconds, stop, then measure your heart rate.							
Wait one minute and measure your heart rate again. (This measures your heart's recovery time.)							
Wait one more minute and measure your heart rate again.							

Name _____ Date _____

How Fit Are You?

The following testing should be done under the supervision of an adult. Make sure you are properly executing each movement so you do not cause injury to yourself. Take these tests before starting your personal exercise program, then about two weeks into a consistent program, take these tests again. This is a great way to monitor your progress.

FITNESS TEST	INSTRUCTIONS	MY RESULTS	
		Test 1	Test 2
FLEXIBILITY	**Sit and Reach Test:** While sitting with your legs straight out in front of you, measure how far you can reach while trying to touch your toes. For this test, keep your knees straight without bending them.	Date: ❑ Knees ❑ Shins ❑ Toes	Date: ❑ Knees ❑ Shins ❑ Toes
CARDIO-VASCULAR	**The Mile Run:** How long does it take you to run one mile? (Only do this if you have been fairly active and do not have any medical problems.) Monitor your speed of recovery by measuring your heart rate immediately when finishing the run and at 30-second intervals after finishing.	Date: Heart Rate: Recovery Time:	Date: Heart Rate: Recovery Time:
	The Step Test: Use stairs or a bench that you set up next to a wall (to keep it from moving). For 30 seconds step up and down on the stair or bench. Measure your heart rate (beats per minute) and then measure your recovery time by measuring your heart rate at 30-second intervals. Record your information.	Date: Heart Rate: Recovery Time:	Date: Heart Rate: Recovery Time:
MUSCULAR	How many sit-ups can you do in one minute?	Date: Sit-Ups:	Date: Sit-Ups:
	How many push-ups can you do in one minute?	Date: Push-Ups:	Date: Push-Ups:
RESTING HEART RATE	The speed at which your heart pumps blood is one of the most important measurements of your body's condition and performance. The two best times to take your pulse every day are: (1) immediately upon awakening and (2) immediately after an aerobic workout. Your resting pulse is a good indicator of your cardiovascular fitness. People with low resting heart rates (60 and under) are usually in good condition. Measure your resting heart rate in the morning before getting out of bed. Place your second and third fingers lightly across your carotid artery (side of neck). Count the number of beats in six seconds and multiply this number by 10 to get your heart rate in beats per minute (BMR). Do this every morning for three days and take the average BMR. Record that number. Do this once a month to monitor your fitness level.	Date: Resting Heart Rate BMR:	Date: Resting Heart Rate BMR:
BODY COMPOSI-TION	What is your body's fat vs. lean body weight? It is not how much you weigh on the scale that is important, but how much fat your body must carry. If a weight chart does not consider a person's frame size, do not use that chart to determine your proper body weight.	Date:	Date:
DOCTOR'S PHYSICAL EXAM	A physical exam prior to any regular physical activity is a good idea and is required by many schools and athletic teams.	Date:	

Name _____   Date _____

My Accidental Workout

List the physical activities you enjoy (you may not even do these often but put them down anyway). Then list the physical activities you participate in consistently (3 or more times per week) and how much time you spend doing them. Then write the physical benefit these activities give you. Write a brief paragraph explaining how you think physical exercise will be incorporated into your life as a young adult.

Physical activities I enjoy:

Physical activities I do regularly (3 or more times a week) and the time I spend at each, and the physical benefit that each gives me:

How do I think physical exercise (activity) will be incorporated into my life as a young adult? Older adult?

Name _____   Date _____

Vocabulary

The answers to the following definitions are present in the word search and may be present forwards, backwards, diagonally or reverse diagonally. Note that definition number one has two correct answers and both are in the answer field.

S	E	S	U	R	I	V	N	O	L	Y	P	A	T	H	E	N	A	I	A	H	P
Y	N	N	G	A	B	A	N	A	B	A	C	T	E	R	I	A	N	L	O	Y	H
M	D	E	R	S	I	S	G	E	O	F	A	R	O	D	N	R	I	L	G	P	R
P	I	G	A	T	S	E	L	E	C	R	D	E	T	I	R	A	S	A	L	O	O
L	M	O	F	I	N	S	U	L	I	N	T	Y	P	E	T	W	O	G	R	G	K
E	S	H	R	A	O	A	N	A	D	Y	S	C	N	A	O	P	M	I	S	L	U
G	A	T	H	R	N	H	O	R	P	L	D	E	B	A	R	X	A	T	E	Y	A
E	S	A	E	S	I	D	W	E	U	A	T	A	M	G	R	E	C	N	A	C	L
R	E	P	V	O	N	S	O	L	S	L	Y	R	O	V	E	U	O	N	I	E	G
E	N	A	L	S	F	N	A	U	T	H	L	J	A	R	D	N	X	R	S	M	E
R	T	C	E	L	E	C	O	N	V	I	C	T	I	O	N	S	G	A	V	I	L
A	R	T	D	A	C	I	M	A	L	V	O	M	S	H	A	R	A	L	F	A	E
M	E	B	M	I	T	O	N	D	R	A	N	V	A	S	O	O	C	Y	S	O	U
V	D	A	R	C	I	T	D	U	X	E	G	I	B	E	M	M	L	M	X	I	S
A	O	R	E	A	O	N	I	R	G	C	E	D	I	T	E	U	O	P	T	R	I
C	R	F	G	H	U	E	L	O	I	H	N	R	E	S	T	T	R	H	P	E	N
C	N	H	T	S	S	D	N	R	M	R	I	O	R	Y	P	S	E	O	E	T	A
I	O	P	A	R	T	I	G	Y	G	E	T	X	O	M	Q	B	K	C	H	S	N
N	I	M	O	T	C	S	M	S	D	I	A	E	Y	U	A	U	N	Y	S	E	O
E	S	E	J	R	I	E	R	Y	M	T	L	S	A	I	R	P	A	T	J	L	D
H	A	L	A	C	L	R	O	N	D	S	E	L	X	B	I	H	W	E	L	E	O
T	I	C	H	A	R	Y	H	P	A	N	T	I	B	O	D	I	E	S	M	T	D

1. A tiny particle that may be plant or animal that causes disease (two answers, not together)

2. Any substance that tends to produce cancer; may be natural or man-made

3. A condition occurring or existing at birth

4. A result of HIV infection, abbreviation

5. A hormone produced by the pancreas which controls how the body uses sugar

6. A condition in which the pancreas releases too much insulin

7. A disease in which abnormal cells grow out of control

8. The form of diabetes in which the person is non-insulin dependent where the pancreas does not produce enough insulin to meet the body's needs or the body can't use it correctly

9. A group or mass of abnormal cells

10. A person's strong beliefs on particular issues

11. The type of diabetes in which the body becomes insulin-dependent as little or no insulin is produced by the pancreas

12. The abbreviation for the virus that causes AIDS

13. White blood cells that fight off germs

14. Reactions from your body that indicate it is trying to fight off an invader. These may manifest themselves as a sore throat or stuffy nose.

15. Any condition that negatively affects the healthy and normal functioning of your mind or body

16. The type of disease in which germs spread from one person to another

17. Weakened or destroyed cells of a particular germ that are injected into a person to produce enough antibodies to keep a person from contracting the disease

18. A disease caused by heredity, the environment or a person's lifestyle

19. The abbreviation for a disease that passes from one person to another through sexual contact

20. Produced by your white blood cells to fight off germs

21. Single-celled tiny organisms that attack your body and may cause disease

22. The invaders that are smaller than bacteria and attack individual cells. They are responsible for, among other things, chicken pox, the common cold, measles, and AIDS.

23. A friendly type of bacteria that your body needs

Name _____   Date _____

Advances in Medicine

Research the following diseases and include the following in your report:

- Was there a specific reason for its name?
- What was (is) the process of infection for the disease? (way it was transmitted)
- How widespread was (is) the disease?
- How was the disease stopped?
- Are we at risk today from this disease?

1. The Black Plague

2. Typhoid Fever

3. Tuberculosis

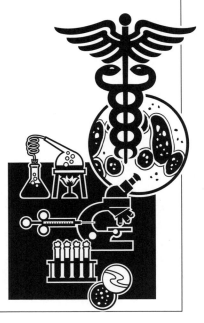

Name _____ Date _____

Fact or Fiction
Looking Into Natural Alternatives
Part I

Natural and homemade remedies have been around for a long time. For example, Mom's chicken soup for a cold and grandma's onion poultice for an earache. Today there is an increase of natural medicines available as over-the-counter remedies. These products often make claims that may or may not be true.

Define the following terms:

1.   Herbs:

2.   Medication:

3.   FDA:

4.   Homeopathy:

5.   Prescription:

6.   Tincture:

7.   Over-the-counter:

8.   Natural or Alternative medicine:

9.   Disclaimer:

10. Claim:

11. Drug:

Name _____ Date _____

Fact or Fiction
Looking Into Natural Alternatives
Part II

Go to your local health food store, pharmacy or the pharmacy section of your grocery store and fill in the following chart with the information you find. List the drugs and natural remedies, their claims and disclaimers for the listed illnesses. You may want to talk to the pharmacist to help you.

ILLNESS	REMEDIES	THE CLAIM(S)	THE DISCLAIMER(S)
THE COMMON COLD	1-2 Drugs:		
	Natural Remedies:		
THE FLU	1-2 Drugs:		
	Natural Remedies:		
SORE THROAT	1-2 Drugs:		
	Natural Remedies:		
EARACHE/ EAR INFECTION	1-2 Drugs:		
	Natural Remedies:		
COUGH	1-2 Drugs:		
	Natural Remedies:		
FEVER	1-2 Drugs:		
	Natural Remedies:		

Summary: If you were thinking about using a "natural remedy" for an illness you had, what two things could you do to know if it was safe to use these alternative medicines?

Name _____ Date _____

The War on Disease

The medical field consists of doctors who have specialized areas of study. Match the field of the specialization on the left with its corresponding description on the right.

____ Oncology

____ Hematology

____ Cardiology

____ Chiropractic

____ Dermatology

____ Gastroenterology

____ Otolaryngology

____ Geriatrics

____ Pediatrics

____ Ophthalmology

____ Osteopathic

____ Obstetrics

____ Endocrinology

____ Neurology

____ Nephrology

____ Psychiatry

____ Podiatry

____ Naturopathy

A. The study of the causes, development, characteristics, and treatment of cancer

B. The branch of medicine that deals with the diseases and malfunctions of the foot and its related structures

C. The medical specialty concerned with the normal functioning of the kidneys

D. The study of the digestive system and diseases and disorders affecting it

E. The medical specialty concerned with care of the elderly

F. The study of blood and disorders of the blood

G. A form of alternative medicine based on the principle that disease is due to the accumulation of waste products and toxins in the body. Practitioners believe that health is maintained by avoiding anything artificial or unnatural in the diet.

H. The branch of medicine concerned with pregnancy, childbirth, and postnatal care

I. A theory of healing based on the belief that disease results from a lack of normal nerve function with physical manipulation and adjustment of the spine for therapy

J. The study of the function of the heart

K. The branch of medicine concerned with the study, prevention, and treatment of mental illness

L. The study of the glands and the hormones they secrete

M. The diagnosis and treatment that recognizes the role of the musculoskeletal system in the healthy functioning of the human body

N. The study of skin diseases.

O. The study of the eyes, ears, nose, and throat.

P. The branch of study concerned with the growth and development of children

Q. The study of the nervous system and its disorders

R. The study of the eye and the diagnosis and treatment of its disorders

Name _____ Date _____

My Physical Defenses Against Disease

Briefly explain the physical defenses your body has to fight against disease and infection.

Eyes: _____
_____
_____
_____

Nose: _____
_____
_____
_____

Mouth: _____
_____
_____

Spleen: _____
_____
_____
_____

Abdomen, stomach: _____
_____
_____
_____

Skin: _____
_____
_____
_____

Fever: _____
_____
_____

Name _____   Date _____

My Convictions
Part 1

The faith that you have, have as your own conviction before God.
Romans 14:22, NAS

What Are Some of Your Present Convictions?

The apostle Paul wanted the Christians in Rome to have personal convictions. A conviction is a strong, settled, and sincere belief that something's right. Do you have any convictions right now? Read the following "I" statements and circle each one for which you presently hold a strong conviction. Please be honest. Don't mark the statements that you feel you "should" have convictions about, but only the ones that you presently do hold strong convictions about.

✟ I believe that the God of the Bible exists.

✟ I sincerely think that Jesus healed the sick and did miracles.

✟ I'm convinced that Jesus died on the cross for my sins.

✟ I'm persuaded that Jesus rose from the dead.

✟ I have a strong opinion that non-Christians need Jesus Christ.

✟ I know for sure that I'm a born-again Christian and am going to heaven.

Identifying Convictions from Scripture and Beginning to Form Your Own

Describe in your own words what type of conviction(s) would be appropriate to develop from the following verses. Give one reason why you agree or disagree with each one.

1. *Psalm* 15:1,3, "Lord, who may abide in your tabernacle?...He who does not backbite with his tongue..."
   A conviction against:_____
   I agree/disagree with this because:

2. *Genesis* 6:11
   A conviction against:_____ and _____
   I agree/disagree with this because:

3. *Matthew* 6:6, "But you, when you pray, go into your room..."
   A conviction about:_____
   I agree/disagree with this because:

(cont. ➥*)*

4. *Ephesians* 6:1-3
    A conviction about:_____
    I agree/disagree with this because:

5. *Ephesians* 5:18, "And be not drunk with wine in which is dissipation [waste]; but be filled with the Spirit..."
    A conviction against:_____, along with a conviction for: _____
    I agree/disagree with this because:

My Convictions
Part 2

How Do You Think That A Teenager Forms Personal Convictions?

You form your personal convictions from the input you receive from your:

✓ Parents	✓ Teachers	✓ Pastors
✓ Environment	✓ Media	✓ Personal experiences
✓ Music	✓ Literature	✓ Friends
✓ Sermons	✓ The Bible	✓ Mistakes

Not everything from these areas automatically becomes one of your core values. Only the values that you make your own become your inner convictions.

Question 1. How would this fact apply to the words of Jesus in *Matthew* 15:19, "For *out of the heart* proceed evil thoughts, murders, adulteries, fornications, thefts, false witness, blasphemies?"

We can assume that just as the heart is the source of bad things, it can also be the source of your Bible-based convictions!

Do You Think That It's Important for Young Teenagers to Form Personal Convictions? Why or Why Not?

Jerry and Chelsea never thought that they would go "all the way", but they did. No one had ever told them how powerful emotions could be. Neither of them had thought about dating standards before they started going steady. Neither had formed any Christ-centered convictions about dating behavior. Both Chelsea and Jerry feel tremendous guilt over their actions. Neither one feels he/she can talk to their parents or to God about their situation.

It's very important for teens to begin to form biblical convictions as early as possible because temptation comes today at earlier and earlier ages.

Question 2. What do the following verses tell you about the importance of forming convictions when you're young and, hopefully, before you find yourself in a direct battle against temptation?

• *I John* 2:14, "I have written to you, young men, because you are strong, and the word of God abides in you, and you have overcome the wicked one."

• *Proverbs* 4:23, "Keep [guard] your heart with all diligence, for out of it spring the issues of [your] life."

(cont. ➡)

- *Matthew* 13:20-21, "But he who received the seed on stony places, this is he who hears the word and immediately receives it with joy; yet he has no root in himself, but endures only for a while."

Focus: What Convictions Do You Have Right Now Concerning Physical Boundaries with the Opposite Sex Before Marriage?

Many teens don't know how far is "too far". Do you have any personal convictions about what is appropriate dating behavior for Christian couples before they get married? If you had a friend who had no dating convictions, what would you tell him/her?

Question 3. Read the following six verses and explain how you might apply each verse to the creation of your personal dating convictions. Read all eight verses of the text before answering so you can understand the context.

- *I Thessalonians* 4:1-8

   4:1   "...walk and to please God...."

   4:3   "For this is the will of God, your sanctification: that you should abstain from sexual immorality..."

   4:4   "...know how to possess his own vessel in sanctification and honor..."

   4:5   "...not in passion of lust..."

   4:6   "...that no one should take advantage of and defraud [go beyond] his brother [or sister] in this matter..."

   4:7   ...For God did not call us to uncleanness, but in holiness."

Name _____ Date _____

An Interview with My Parent(s)

It is important for you to understand your parents' convictions on certain issues. This will help you better understand them and will help you while you are developing your own beliefs concerning these issues.

Ask your parents the following questions. Write their answers on a separate sheet of paper. Remember that they may want this to be confidential, so keep these answers to yourself. When you finish the interview, explain what you believe about each issue—do you agree with your parents or disagree and why?

"What is your conviction about lying?"

Do you remember an instance in your childhood or as a young adult when lying was ever an issue? Is it ever okay to not tell the truth? Do you ever find it difficult personally to stand by this conviction? What do you do when you find it difficult?

"What is your conviction about stealing?"

Do you remember your parent(s) talking to you about stealing? How old were you when you developed any conviction about it? If I were ever tempted to steal something, what would you tell me to help me?

"What is your conviction about watching movies, television and/or videos?"

When did you form a conviction concerning entertainment like this? When you were a teenager did an instance ever come up when you needed to talk to your parent(s) about what you wanted to watch or see? Did you ever have a hard time with your parents' boundaries for you in this area? How did you handle this and what would you tell me concerning this area?

"What is your conviction concerning physical contact with the opposite sex prior to marriage?"

Do you remember having this conversation with your parents when you were younger? At what age(s) did you talk to your parents about it? Did you find it hard to follow their boundaries set for you? When did you feel you formed your own personal convictions concerning this area? What would you like to share with me concerning this issue?

Name _____   Date _____

Vocabulary

Next to each of the seven words below, write the corresponding letter of the definition from the bottom of the page that best describes the word. Not all of the definitions apply to the words from the list.

Pride _____

Self-esteem _____

Personal identity _____

Jealousy _____

Mature _____

Character _____

Confident _____

a. Feelings that we have not received our fair share

b. A belief that we are better than we really are

c. An understanding of who we are through Christ

d. Suspicion that others are intent on undermining our efforts

e. An absence of feelings of inferiority or feeling "less than"

f. A mocking, cartoon-like representation of a person's efforts

g. The feeling of resentment toward another person for a talent or possession they have that you wish for yourself

h. Who you really are, even when no one is observing you

i. A fear that we may be overlooked for a promotion or award

j. The way you feel about yourself

k. To grow spiritually, socially, emotionally, mentally and physically

l. To belittle the efforts of others; to cause them humiliation

Name _____ Date _____

Interview: "Mom or Dad, Have You Ever Felt...?"

Choose to talk to either your Mother or your Father. Make sure that he or she is not distracted with doing something else. Ask the following questions and then ask what he or she did about his or her feelings. Assure your Dad or Mom that you will hold what you hear confidential.

"Have You Ever Felt...and What Did You Do About It?"

❑ ...uncertain about what others thought of you?

❑ ...unable to keep a certain friend or group of friends?

❑ ...inadequate to make decisions?

❑ ...doubtful about yourself?

❑ ...fearful about your future?

❑ ...uninterested in school?

❑ ...uninterested in God and/or church activities?

❑ ...tired of getting up in the morning?

❑ ...worried or somewhat depressed?

❑ ...isolated and all alone?

❑ ...misunderstood by others?

❑ ...stressed-out from all of the changes happening in your life?

• What have you learned about your parent(s) that you did not know before?

• In light of what you have heard from your parent(s), what insights have you learned that you can apply to your own life?

Name _____ Date _____

How to Replace Worry with Faith and Peace

BIBLE STUDY

"I'm facing some problems with grades. I used to be a straight 'A' student. But, now I'm a little above average. That makes me feel very bad."
Tim, age 14

"I'm struggling with fear of where I'm going when I die. I know that if I have Jesus in my heart, I'll go to heaven; it's just that I'm not sure He's there."
Stephanie, age 14

Tim is worried about his grades. Stephanie is worried about her salvation. Teens have many pressures in their lives today that cause them emotional stress and inner tension. If you want to replace your worries with faith and peace, just practice the following five steps.

1. **Know what worry is and learn how to recognize it in yourself.**

   How does the dictionary define the term worry?

   How can you tell you might be worrying about certain things?

2. **Write down some of the areas in your life that you are worried about right now.**

3. **Read what Jesus said about the basic necessities of life and how His words might also apply to your own areas of worry which you listed above:**

   So my counsel is: Don't worry about things—food, drink, and clothes. For you already have life and a body—and they are far more important than what to eat and wear. Look at the birds! They don't worry about what to eat—they don't need to sow or reap or store up food—for your heavenly Father feeds them. And you are far more valuable to Him than they are. Will all your worries add a single moment to your life? And why worry about your clothes? Look at the field lilies! They don't worry about theirs. Yet King Solomon in all his glory was not clothed as beautifully as they. And if God cares so wonderfully for flowers that are here today and gone tomorrow, won't He more surely care for you, O men of little faith? (Matthew 6:25-30, TLB)

   (cont. ➥)

According to Jesus, what are the three things that you don't have to worry about?

Do you think this includes other areas of your life as well?

What are the three reasons that Jesus gives (in the verses above) as to why Christians don't have to worry?

Now read the rest of the passage:

So don't worry at all about having enough food and clothing. Why be like the heathen? For they take pride in all these things and are deeply concerned about them. But your heavenly Father already knows perfectly well that you need them, and He will give them to you if you give Him first place in your life and live as He wants you to. So don't be anxious about tomorrow. God will take care of your tomorrow too. Live one day at a time. [Each day has enough trouble of its own.—KJV]. (*Matthew 6:31-34, TLB*)

What does Jesus say is, oftentimes, at the heart of an unbeliever's worry and focus on obtaining the material necessities of life?

What does Jesus say are the two conditions (the "if's") of God sovereignly taking care of believers?

Why would Jesus warn you against "borrowing trouble"?

4. Know what faith is and appreciate how it increases in your life.

When you know what faith is and really want to grow in your trust in God, faith will begin to replace worry in your life. The author of *Hebrews* defines faith below. Look the verse up in several Bible translations, if you are able, to see how the Bible defines faith.

Now faith is the substance of things hoped for, the evidence of things not seen (Hebrews 11:1, KJV). What is faith? It is the confident assurance that something we want is going to happen. It is the certainty that what we hope for is waiting for us, even though we cannot see it up ahead (Hebrews 11:1, NKJV).

(cont. ➥)

Name _____   Date _____

How to Replace Worry with Faith and Peace (*cont.*)

BIBLE STUDY

How does the dictionary define the term faith?

In your own words, explain what faith means to you:

All Christians have problems and challenges. God allows these trials to come into our lives to help us to grow in faith. You can grow in faith with each new challenge if you'll:

(1) admit to God how worried you are about your problems; (2) let go of how much you try to control your own life and give Him control; and, (3) increase in your ability to turn your problems over to Him sooner and better the next time.

5. Read Paul's secret to a worry-free life and begin to practice it.

Don't worry about anything; instead, pray about everything; tell God your needs and don't forget to thank Him for His answers. If you do this, you will experience God's peace, which is far more wonderful than the human mind can understand. His peace will keep your thoughts and your hearts quiet and at rest as you trust in Christ Jesus. (*Philippians 4:6-7, TLB*)

What does Paul say you should do to replace worry with peace?

How does Paul actually describe the answer to the above question?

What benefit will come to your thoughts and your emotions ("your hearts") when you practice the answer to the first question?

Choose one of the benefits from the above question and define it from the dictionary. How can it apply to your life?

Name ______________________ Date ____________

How to Overcome Negative Self-Talk

Your life is made up of "facts" and "interpretations of facts". One fact is that you are not a perfect person. You make mistakes. We all do. You choose every day, however, to give this fact one of two different interpretations. The interpretations you give to this—and other facts in your life like the way you look or the talents you have—we call "self-talk". "Self-talk" are the "tapes" that you allow to run in your head. They are the interpretations or the "spins" that you choose to give to the experiences that you have. They are the personal "filters"—the rose-colored glasses—through which you choose to give meaning to what happens in your life. From the fact that you do make mistakes, you could say to yourself, "I'm a lousy person", or you could say, "I'm a normal human being." When you tell yourself, "I'm a lousy person", this is negative self-talk. Negative self-talk can make you begin to feel sad, mad, or depressed. When you tell yourself, "I'm a normal human being," this is positive (and biblical) self-talk. Both kinds of self-talk will eventually affect your actions. Although you cannot control what others say about you, you can control how much you let what they say affect you. Have you ever told yourself that you were a bad person because you had a negative experience? This is what both Tammy and Bob did in the following two examples. These stories can help you understand the impact that your self-talk has on your feelings of self-worth. Notice the choice that you always have in choosing either positive or negative self-talk—no matter what mistakes you might make. At the end of each story, note the "fact" and then the two "interpretations" of the fact from which they had to choose.

(cont. ➻)

#1 Tammy knew about her social studies report way in advance of the due date. Two days before her report was due, she went to the library with the intention of spending all day finishing it. When she arrived at the library, she found that all of the resources she needed were already checked out! Because Tammy had procrastinated until the last minute, she failed to get her report turned in on time. The thoughts that ran through Tammy's mind reinforced the negative feelings that she already had about her self-worth. "I'm so stupid," she thought, "I can't ever seem to do anything right. My parents are going to hate me for this."

The Fact: "I failed to turn in my social studies report on time."

The Negative Interpretation of the Fact (Negative Self-talk): "I'm so stupid. I never seem to do anything right. My parents are going to hate me for this."

The Positive Interpretation of the Fact (Positive Self-talk): "I made a mistake in not planning ahead more for my report. I will ask my teacher for an extension. Next time, I'll start sooner."

#2 Bob studied for his driver's license test for several months. When the big day came, he felt insecure and nervous. When he got into the driver's seat, his sister's criticisms of his driving went through his mind: "You are so uncoordinated. Can't you get it right? I bet you'll never pass the test." As the driving instructor asked Bob to parallel park, his mind blanked out. He took four tries to park the car. Bob failed his driving test. "I'm such a failure," Bob mumbled as his Mother drove him home.

The Fact: "I failed my driver's test."

The Negative Interpretation of the Fact (Negative Self-talk): "I'm a lousy driver. I'll probably fail my driver's test each time I take it. I'm a failure as a teen."

The Positive Interpretation of the Fact (Positive Self-talk): "I failed my driver's test the first time I took it. I believed that I was a bad driver because of what my sister told me. I'm not going to believe that anymore. I'm going to practice parallel parking some more and then take the test again as soon as I can."

(cont. ➥)

Name _____   Date _____

How to Overcome Negative Self-Talk (cont.)

Listed below are ten statements which are examples of negative self-talk recordings you might be familiar with. Each is a reflection of one or more of the following untruths:

a. "I must meet certain standards to feel good about myself."

b. "I must be accepted by certain people (significant others in my life) to feel good about myself."

c. "Those who fail (including myself) are unworthy of love and deserve to be blamed and condemned."

d. "I am what I am. I cannot change. I am hopeless. I will never amount to anything."

Study the following statements. Ask yourself: "What false belief(s) does this statement represent?" Beside each statement, place the letter of one or more of the false beliefs from the above list, that best correspond(s) with the statement.

____1.   "My sister is right. I'll never do anything right. I'm such a failure."

____2.   "I'm so undisciplined. I'll never be able to accomplish anything."

____3.   "I will never be able to trust God."

____4.   "No one important in my class wants to hang out with me."

____5.   "I don't have any musical ability like my friends. I don't do anything well."

____6.   "I failed math. I'll always be stupid."

____7.   "I can't overcome this sin."

____8.   "I really don't deserve friends anyway. I'm such a loser."

____9.   "I will never be able to please my parents."

____10. "No one will ever like me. I am so ugly."

Name ____________________ Date ____________

Grow in Openness to God

Every day at recess, a group of Steven's classmates hung out in the forested area just outside the school property, which was against the school's rules.

"Aren't you going to come with us? No one will see us!" they all laughed as they headed toward the trees. Steven heard their remarks, "Steven is such a 'goody goody'."

Because the teasing got worse each day, Steven shared his feelings of frustration with God. He asked God for strength to stay on campus because he really wanted to go with them even though he knew it was not right. One day, the teacher on duty noticed the group walk off campus. She immediately reported them to the Principal. Steven watched as all of his friends were escorted to the Principal's office. Steven went home and told his Mom how his classmates had been going off campus and had finally been caught.

"Did your friends laugh at you when you chose not to go with them?" his mother asked.

"Well, sure," he replied.

"How did that make you feel?" she continued.

"It was harder and harder for me not to go off campus with them, until I shared with God how I was feeling and asked Him for strength. I'm really learning how being as open with God as I would with my best friend really works."

Steven's openness with God when he was struggling inside is a great example to follow. Do you ever find yourself wanting to give in to temptations that you know just aren't right? In the Bible, God calls David "a man after His own heart"(*I Samuel* 13:14), because David was open and honest in his relationship with God. He saw God as his true friend. This is the kind of relationship God wants with you.

Steven had the heart attitude which cared more about what God thought than what others thought. How can you learn to view God as your true friend?

1. What makes someone a true friend?

2. How might a person be a true friend to God?

(*cont.* ➸)

3. What are some things that you think are important to God?

4. How can you show God that you care about what is important to Him?

In the Bible, God reveals what He thinks is important. What God values often differs from what society values.

5. What things does society see as valuable?

6. Write out *I Samuel* 13:14; 16:7.

7. In contrast to what society values, what is God concerned about in you?

8. Write out *II Chronicles* 16:9.

If you desire to have more of a friendship with God in which you can be more open and honest, ask God to help you. Just as Steven found that being open with God gave Him the strength to do what was right, you can develop the same kind of relationship with God. The next time you talk with God, you may want to pray something like:

> *"Lord, I want to get to know you more, to learn about what you are like and what a friendship with you really means. To be honest Lord, I really don't know exactly what it means to have a heart after your own heart. O Lord, would You please help me to be more open with you and care more about those things that are important to You? Thank you, Lord. Amen."*

Name _____   Date _____

Vocabulary

Write the missing word in the blank in each sentence from the list below. Not all of the words from the list apply to one of the sentences.

A. David made a list of steps he would need to accomplish over time in order to achieve his _____.

B. Terri knew that her questions had been too personal and invasive. She felt that she had crossed a _____ her friend had established for herself.

C. Ron knew if he allowed himself to be drawn into the argument, it would _____ him from the project he was trying to complete.

D. It took all of her _____ to avoid saying something hurtful after what had happened between her and her sister.

E. His _____ would be put into motion soon by following through on the plans he had made for the immediate future.

F. In order to make a list of plans and follow through in our lives, it is important that we have a clear understanding of our ultimate _____.

Repentance	Acquisition
Long-term goal	Self-control
Goal	Boundary
Limitations	Short-term goal
Forgiveness	Distract

Name _____ Date _____

Identifying and Facing Your Fears

It was the first day of school. As I entered my new seventh grade classroom, my stomach tightened and my hands began to sweat. "What is this year going to be like?" I thought as I took my assigned seat.
Susan, age 14

What Fears Can Do To You...

Fear can save or destroy your life! If you fear to enter into a dangerous or tempting situation, you'll keep yourself safe. In this study, however, we will look at the negative side of this strong emotion. Here are some negative things that the wrong kind of fear can do to your life.

- Fear can keep you frozen.

- Fear can keep you from enjoying life.

- Fear can keep you from taking appropriate risks.

- Fear can keep you from sharing honestly with God or others.

- Fear can keep you from developing or learning a new skill.

- Fear can keep you from anything competitive.

- Fear can keep you from fulfilling your destiny in God!

What else have you noticed that the feelings of fear can do to you?

Identifying Your Own Fears...

Of the following list, place a check mark by any fear(s) you have ever experienced—or are now experiencing—in your life.

- ❑ The fear of failure

- ❑ The fear of what others think of you

- ❑ The fear of disappointing your parent(s)

- ❑ The fear of disappointing God

- ❑ The fear of getting punished

- ❑ The fear of being rejected ("No one will like me.")

- ❑ The fear of being physically or emotionally hurt

(cont. ➥)

- ❑ The fear of losing someone you love

- ❑ The fear of sickness

- ❑ The fear of dying

- ❑ The fear of going to hell

- ❑ The fear of _____ (any other fear not listed above that you may be feeling)

Overcoming your own fears or anxieties is a process that is very personal and unique. The anxiety you may experience over going to the dentist, for example, may be overcome by bravely facing the dentist. Your fear may become less and less prominent as you realize "That wasn't as bad as I thought." Your fears of the dentist will probably be reinforced each time you have a painful experience in the dentist chair. No two people handle their fears or anxieties in exactly the same manner. This is one reason why it is very important not to compare the way you handle your fears with the way your peers handle their personal anxieties.

Facing and Overcoming Your Fears...

Many of your fears are based upon the painful experiences of your past. Each positive experience you have in any area of fear in your life, however, will help to drain away some of fear's power. Read the stories below and answer the questions that follow.

One day as he was leaving school, Pat spied a skateboard near the cafeteria door. He hadn't been able to afford a skateboard, and his parents felt that they were too dangerous. So, Pat decided to take the skateboard since no one was around to notice. After skateboarding on the professional jumps in the nearby park for a long time, Pat decided to try the hardest jump at the park. As he made his final approach, Pat suddenly felt a pang of guilt for taking someone else's skateboard. This thought distracted his focus just long enough to cause him to veer off of the ramp and over the edge. He hit the ground hard. God had gotten his attention!—but Pat was too scared to tell God that he had stolen someone else's skateboard. He felt that God would be so disappointed in him. Finally, after feeling a lot of inner frustration about it, he confessed his sin to God and felt an instantaneous release of joy in his heart when he told God that tomorrow he would return the board to where he had found it.

1. What did Pat fear in this story?

2. How do you think that Pat's eventually positive experience of confession and restitution (his returning the skateboard) will affect Pat the next time he needs to confess a sin to God?

(cont. ➤➤)

Name _____   Date _____

Identifying and Facing Your Fears (cont.)

Angie stayed up late talking to her friends on the phone. A couple of new girls had just come to the school and she was extra excited about getting to know them. Before she knew it, she had to go to bed without studying for her English test the next day. The last thing she wanted was to get a low grade on a test. She knew that if she failed the test, her Dad and Mom would get really angry at her. To avoid possibly failing the exam, Angie took some "cheat sheets" into the classroom with her. Angie received an "A" on the test. Inside her conscience, however, Angie didn't feel very comfortable. She told herself, "Why did I do something so stupid? I've never cheated on an exam before in my entire life!"

1. What did Angie fear in this incident?

2. What did Angie choose to allow her fear to do to her?

Tony and Pete had known each other all of their lives. They grew up in the same neighborhood. Their Dads were old fishing buddies. When they started to attend Lake Avenue Junior High School, however, everything began to change. Pete got in with the wrong crowd. He started spending time with some eighth graders who would go into the woods after school to smoke and look at pornography. Pete wanted Tony to come and join them since it was "cool" to hang out with eighth graders. Tony went with Pete once, but after he saw what they were doing, he felt really torn inside. He didn't want to go with the guys to the woods, but he feared that Pete would no longer be his friend if he didn't go. His fear of being rejected by Pete won out, and he joined Pete and the guys every day.

1. What did Tony fear Pete would do to him if he didn't go out to the woods with him and the guys?

2. If you had been Tony, what would you have done with your fear about Pete instead of going out into the woods?

(cont. ➤➤)

Chris lives with his Dad, Jack. He hurt a lot when his parents split up five years ago, but he's very happy that he has a good relationship with them. One evening, his Dad invited a Christian lady from church over to their house for dinner. To prepare for her arrival, Chris set the table as his Dad stirred the onions into the spaghetti sauce. The lady arrived and Chris was very polite as his Dad introduced him to a very kind-looking lady named Janet. After Chris showed Janet his newest computer game, Chris' Dad called them to the table to eat. Toward the end of the dinner, Jack told Chris that he had something that he wanted to tell him. Chris sat up to hear. His Dad shared that he and Janet were going to be seriously dating. Chris was shocked and a deep fear began to grip him. His Dad asked him what was wrong.

Before he could even think about his reaction, Chris blurted out, "I'm afraid that if you two get married, you and Janet might get a divorce just like you and Mom did!"

His Dad quickly rebuffed him: "You shouldn't feel that way, Chris, that's stupid. You shouldn't let such negative fears be in your head—not even for a second! What's wrong with you?" Chris went to his room and cried.

1. What was Chris' fear?

2. What was Jack's response to Chris' fear?

3. If you had been Chris, how would Jack's comments to you about your fear have made you feel?

4. If you had been Jack, would you have changed your comment to Chris? If so, how would you have re-worded it?

From these previous examples, summarize what you have learned about how to handle fear.

Name _____ Date _____

What is True Success?

BIBLE STUDY

Look up the following Bible references and write them in the space provided. Answer the questions that follow each verse. Also, summarize what that verse means to you and how you can apply it to your life.

Proverbs 28:6

1. Do you know of anyone who obtained their money by lying, cheating, stealing, or some other illegal means? If so, who? How did they make their money?

2. What role, if any, do you feel that God had in the obtaining of their wealth?

3. How can this verse apply to your own personal life?

Proverbs 22:4

1. What does the word "honor" mean? What is the difference between the human honor that our culture gives to people and the honor which God gives?

2. John the Baptist died at a young age because Herod had him beheaded in prison. How could his short life still be considered a success?

3. How can this verse apply to your own personal life?

(cont. ➻)

I Corinthians **9:25**

1. Have you ever had a goal for which you had to give up something else to obtain? If so, what was your goal and what did you have to give up?

2. Have you ever received a ribbon or trophy for placing in some athletic event? If so, what was the event, and where did you place? Do you still have the ribbon or trophy? Do you think that you'll still have it ten years from now? What could this teach you about earthly rewards?

3. How can this verse apply to your own personal life?

Name _____ Date _____

Steps to Making Wise Decisions

Introduction

Write out *Proverbs* 9:10-11:

1. Why do you think that knowing God results in every other kind of understanding?

2. How can having more wisdom make your life more fruitful and profitable?

How to Make Wise Decisions

1. Gather Information: Do Your Homework!

Your Goal: To find as many facts and ideas as possible about a problem to be solved or an idea to be investigated.

> Jim finally had saved enough money to purchase the computer game that he had wanted for months. As he was headed out the door to the mall to make his big purchase, the phone rang. It was his best friend, Josh, with tickets to a championship basketball game between two of Jim's favorite teams. The cost of the ticket was the same as the cost of the computer game he wanted. Jim would have to make a choice. If he decided to spend his money on the basketball ticket, he would have to start all over again to save up for the computer game. Answer the following questions to find out what kind of information Jim needs to make the wisest decision with his money.

A. What information might Jim need to help him with this difficult decision?

(cont. ➨)

B. Who might Jim talk to in order to gain more wisdom about his decision about the game?

C. Do you think that Jim should tell Josh his dilemma? Why or why not?

D. Do you think God really cares how Jim spends his money? How might Jim pray for wisdom concerning this decision?

2. Get Input from God.

Your Goal: Give God the opportunity to reveal His thoughts about a problem to be solved or an idea to be investigated.

Rebecca felt that her friendship with Amy had begun to turn sour. Amy seemed much more interested in boys than Rebecca felt comfortable with. All Amy wanted to do was call popular boys from their class and hang out with them at the mall on the weekends. One weekend, Amy wanted Rebecca to tell her parents that she would be spending the night at her house only to sneak out and attend a high school party where alcohol would be served. Luckily, Rebecca's family was already planning to go away for the weekend. Rebecca had a good excuse to say "no". Next time, Rebecca may not be so fortunate. Rebecca is not sure if she needs to cut off the friendship with Amy or just let things continue. Every time she talks to Amy at school or on the phone, Rebecca feels uneasy and concerned about what Amy is getting involved in.

A. What kind of information does Rebecca need to know about her decision concerning Amy? Does she need any further information?

B. Who might Rebecca talk to so as to gain more wisdom about her decision about Amy?

C. If Rebecca decides to cut off her friendship with Amy, what consequences should Rebecca be prepared for?

D. If Rebecca decides not to cut off her friendship with Amy, what consequences should Rebecca be prepared for?

(cont. ➠)

Name _____   Date _____

Steps to Making Wise Decisions (cont.)

E. Is there anything else that Rebecca might do to help her with this decision?

F. How might Rebecca pray for wisdom concerning this difficult decision?

To help you answer this question, first read *James* 1:5-6 in *The Living Bible*.

"If you want to know what God wants you to do, ask Him, and He will gladly tell you, for He is always ready to give a bountiful supply of wisdom to all who ask Him; He will not resent it. But when you ask Him, be sure that you really expect Him to tell you, for a doubtful mind will be as unsettled as a wave of the sea that is driven and tossed by the wind; and every decision you then make will be uncertain, as you turn first this way and then that. If you don't ask with faith, don't expect the Lord to give you any solid answer."

1. According to *James* 1:5, if Rebecca wants to know what God wants her to do, what should she do?

2. What does God say He will do if Rebecca asks Him?

3. From this verse, does it seem that God would want to keep His thoughts about her situation from her or to tell Rebecca?

4.   What kind of attitude would be best for Rebecca to have when she asked God about her circumstance with Amy?

5. If Rebecca didn't ask in faith what might happen to her mind and her ultimate decision?

6. How else might God speak to her other than in her prayer time?

(cont. ➥)

3. Make Your Decision.

Your Goal: To make the best possible choice about what to believe or do.

A. What might be the possible outcome if you procrastinated or waited too long to make your decision?

B. If after gathering information and praying about it, you still do not know what to do, what might you do?

C. If you have not done your homework, and have not taken the time to get input from God concerning your decision, what might be the possible outcome?

4. Evaluate Your Decision.

Your Goal: To learn from your decision.

When evaluating your decision, ask yourself the following questions:

- ❑ "Did I solve my problem?"
- ❑ "Am I happy with the outcome?"
- ❑ "Even if I am not happy with the outcome, am I confident that it was what God wanted for me?"
- ❑ "What did I learn from my experience?"

A. Imagine that Jim decided to go to the game with Josh, why would it be important for Jim to evaluate his decision when he returned from the game?

B. If Rebecca decided to cut off her relationship with Amy, what do you think Rebecca might learn from that decision?

Name ____ Date ______________

How To Set A Realistic Goal

As soon as Carrie walked through the front door of her house after school, she threw her backpack in the corner. She then headed straight for the refrigerator. Carrie grabbed a cold soda, shoved a large bag of her favorite chips under her arm, located the TV remote on the counter, and plopped down on the soft sofa ready to get into her favorite show. "Friday, at last," she sighed with a deep sense of relief.

The weekend passed quickly. When Sunday arrived, Carrie's Mom asked her the usual question: "Did you get all your homework finished this weekend, honey?"

As Carrie reached for her unopened backpack in the corner, she replied, "Sure, Mom, I'm working on it right now!"

Do you ever leave your homework until the last minute only to realize that you don't have enough time to finish it? Does your weekend seem to fly by? Do you ever wonder where all of your money has gone? Do you ever have a difficult time finding an important paper? Without knowing how to set goals or how to reach them, your life can become disorganized and, sometimes, overwhelming. You can learn how to set and reach your goals—if you'll follow some very important principles. You can apply these practical principles to any goal that you want to reach.

Principle #1: Evaluate Your Present Situation.

a. Is my homework usually turned in late? ________

b. Do I leave my homework to the last minute? ________

c. Am I often late for school in the morning? ________

d. Is my school notebook a mess? (papers falling out, unorganized, hard to find assignments)? ________

e. Do I ever forget that I even have homework? ________

f. Am I always on a diet but never seem to lose any weight? ________

g. Do I start projects but have a hard time finishing them? ________

Principle #2: Get Input From Significant Others In Your Life.

a. Do you think I am an organized person? ________

b. What strengths do you think I have?

(cont. ➻)

c. What weaknesses do you think I have?

d. Do you feel I could be trusted to complete an important task? ________

e. Do you think I procrastinate? ________ Why or why not?

Principle #3: Choose A Specific Target Area in Your Life That You Would Like to Improve or Achieve.

Put a check mark in the box in front of the one goal that you would like to set for yourself right now.

"I would like to..."

- ❑ manage my time better.
- ❑ improve my academic performance.
- ❑ improve my physical appearance (lose/gain weight, change eating patterns or habits).
- ❑ keep a consistent exercise program.
- ❑ save money for something specific.
- ❑ learn a musical instrument (or improve a skill I already have).
- ❑ join a competitive sports team (or improve my athletic performance in a sport I already play).
- ❑ set a goal in the following area not mentioned above:
  ____.

Make sure that your goal is realistic. A realistic goal is a target that is practical, specific, and doable. Setting a goal to become the President of the United States would be specific and practical but, in most cases anyway, not doable.

Principle #4: Map Out Your Specific Plan to Reach Your Goal.

The following questions about your goal will help you to make it practical and realistic.

Write the one goal which you have chosen from Principle #3 (above) on the line below:

____

Apply the following questions to the goal which you have chosen from Principle #3 (above) in a brief paragraph. Then, start to accomplish it!

(cont. ➛)

Name ______________________________ Date ______________

How To Set A Realistic Goal (cont.)

1. **Time:** How much time will your goal require of you each day, week, or month? When will you start? When will you schedule it in? In order to reach your goal, list out what other areas of your schedule you might have to change or remove. If your goal is to increase your physical exercise, you might record that you're going to play basketball three afternoons a week from 3:30PM-5:00PM and ride your bike on Saturdays sometime in the early afternoon.

2. **Energy:** How much more energy will you be required to use to accomplish your goal? How do you know that you won't be too tired to try to reach it? What kind of energy will your goal mostly require: mental, physical, or both? If your goal is to improve your academic performance, you might record that you'll need to get to bed by 9:30PM each school night so that you can get up early enough to study before you go to school.

3. **Money:** How much money will reaching this goal cost? What items will you have to purchase? Do you have enough money to do this? If your goal is to learn a musical instrument, how much is your instrument going to cost? Can you find a less expensive one in the newspaper? Can you buy a used set of drums, for example, instead of a new set?

4. **Skill-level:** What types of skills does reaching your goal require? If your goal requires you having a specialized skill before you can accomplish it, when and how will you develop that skill first? If your goal is to join a competitive sports team, do you know the skills that will be required to compete at that level? If you wanted to play basketball, do you already know how to dribble, shoot, and pass?

5. **Specific:** Explain how your goal is specific. A physical health goal to "get better" is too general. A goal that says, "only to drink one soda per week", is specific.

6. **Desire:** What kind of strong willpower will you need to reach this goal? Do you already have the inner desire to accomplish it? If your goal was to lose weight, what will keep you motivated to avoid the high-fat foods that taste so delicious? If your goal is to gain weight, what will give you the desire to keep doing the muscle-building exercises required?

(*cont.* ➻)

7. **Teamwork:** Who will you need to help you accomplish your goal? If you'll need to catch a ride from one of your parents in order to get to the gym, are your parents just as committed to helping you reach your goal as you are? If your goal is to save so much money each week in order to buy something you really want, will your parents be willing to pay you a weekly allowance for doing your chores?

Principle #5: Evaluate and Re-evaluate Your Goals.

As you are taking steps to reach a specific goal, evaluate your progress by asking yourself the following questions:

- How is my progress (am I on target) in reaching this goal?

- Do I still have the motivation to continue this goal? If not, what can I do to get motivated?

- Is this goal still realistic?

- What changes do I need to make to accomplish my goal?

Name _____   Date _____

Vocabulary

The answers to the following definitions are present in the word search and may be present forwards, backwards, diagonally or reverse diagonally.

C	H	O	K	M	N	O	N	V	E	R	B	A	L	E	S	B	P
A	O	D	I	S	R	E	S	P	E	C	T	I	R	N	L	N	A
I	N	F	A	T	U	A	T	I	O	N	H	T	O	D	L	O	R
H	O	H	R	N	T	S	L	M	A	L	K	I	T	O	A	I	O
G	P	A	T	E	C	H	A	Y	A	H	T	E	Z	N	W	T	K
E	H	D	I	S	E	V	A	M	G	U	G	D	I	T	S	A	E
V	A	I	F	H	P	A	M	O	T	E	Q	E	V	A	U	C	T
I	N	P	I	H	S	N	O	I	T	A	L	E	R	J	O	I	H
T	I	H	C	N	E	H	T	C	A	I	H	S	E	M	Y	N	N
I	M	C	I	O	R	S	A	E	A	R	O	T	A	H	E	U	O
S	E	E	A	R	B	G	L	D	O	H	L	L	T	G	R	M	I
O	V	Y	L	U	O	L	A	S	H	I	K	A	A	D	E	M	T
P	I	H	S	D	N	E	I	R	F	U	P	T	B	O	H	O	A
S	G	E	D	U	L	A	C	E	T	M	I	H	P	R	T	C	T
E	R	H	B	Y	N	H	O	H	E	V	A	R	A	S	E	W	U
Y	O	A	R	U	V	E	S	C	E	A	Z	T	E	N	K	V	P
R	F	N	O	Y	I	Z	T	H	T	E	R	E	H	P	I	T	E
D	A	A	T	H	K	O	N	A	H	C	E	G	N	E	V	E	R

1. The type of health that allows you to get along with different types of people.

2. A social connection in which people share interests or activities.

3. A tie with others by blood, marriage, work, or social role.

4. Replacing one person or thing with another.

5. A relationship that exists with something that is not real rather than with an actual living person would be called an _____ relationship.

6. The act of expressing thoughts, feelings, information or beliefs through speech, writing or signs.

7. A type of communication that involves sharing a message through words or talking.

8. Sharing a message without the use of words, such as body language or hand motions would be said to be a form of _____ communication.

9. Barriers between people that hinder their communication.

10. Feeling a strong emotional attraction to a member of the opposite sex.

11. The type of peer pressure you experience when others encourage you to do things that are good for you.

12. When others encourage you to do things that are harmful to you that is a form of _____ peer pressure.

13. Not interfering or intruding upon another person's rights is a way of showing _____.

14. To show a lack of courtesy by being rude or insulting or using sarcasm.

15. What people think of you.

16. The act of getting even with someone.

17. To let go of all of your desire to punish or seek revenge against those who may have hurt of offended you.

18. When you understand the pain of another because you have felt that pain yourself.

Name _____   Date _____

Friendship

Read the following verses about friendship and answer the questions which follow.   BIBLE STUDY

1. **"A mirror reflects a man's face, but what he is really like is shown by the kind of friends he chooses."** *Proverbs* **27:19 (TLB)**

   a. What are some of the ways that you normally use to try to tell what kind of a person someone really is?

   b. Why are the above ways not perfect methods?

   c. What similarities or common interests do you have with your closest friends?

   d. We can refer to what the above verse says about friendship as The Friendship Mirror. Do you feel that The Friendship Mirror can be an accurate way to discern a person's inner character? Why or why not?

2. **"A true friend is always loyal, and a brother [or, sister] is born to help in time of need."** *Proverbs* **17:17 (TLB)**

   a. If there are friends that are "true", do you think that there are also friends that are "false"? If so, what qualities would a "false" friend have that you wouldn't like?

   b. Write down your definition of loyalty.

(cont. ➤➤*)*

c. Which of your friends have been really loyal to you? What did they do to prove or show their loyalty to you?

d. Explain one time that you really felt like you needed the help of your friend(s). If one of your true friends helped you, please explain how.

Name _____   Date _____

Making Sense of "Plug-In Drugs"
Part I: The Electronic Time Inventory
Week One

During the first week of this assignment, keep an accurate record of how much time you spend with electronic entertainment. This includes all time spent with TV, movies, video games, computer games, and the non-educational use of the internet. Write down in the chart below the day, the date, the program or game you watched or played, the time you began watching/playing, the time you stopped, and the total time spent. At the end of the week, add up all of your daily times and enter a total time at the bottom of the chart. If you watch or play more than one time per day, write small and record each time on that day.

Day	Date	Program, Movie, or Game	Time Began	Time Finished	Total Time
					Hrs. Min.
					Hrs. Min.
					Hrs. Min.
					Hrs. Min.
					Hrs. Min.
					Hrs. Min.
					Hrs. Min.
			Total Time for the Week		Hrs. Min.

Name _____ Date _____

Making Sense of "Plug-In Drugs"
Part II: Reflecting on The Electronic Time Inventory: Alternate Time Choices Week Two

1. What was the total amount of time you spent with electronic entertainment during Week One? Hours: _____ Minutes: _____. Was the amount of time that you spent with electronic entertainment during Week One the usual amount of time (on average) that you spend most weeks, or was it a lot higher or lower? Please explain.

2. Look at your worksheet for Part I of this assignment. Notice the specific days and times that you spent with electronic entertainment. Answer the following questions about those days and times on a day-by-day basis in the chart below. For example, record what other invitations (see column one below) you received during the same time that you were with electronic entertainment; what books you chose not to read; what time you chose not to spend with friends, family, etc.

Day	Invitations	Activities/ Reading Books	Hobbies/ Goals/ Games	Grades/ Homework	Friends	Family	Youth Group/ Church	Sports Events	Ministry/ Service
Monday									
Tuesday									
Wednesday									
Thursday									
Friday									
Saturday									
Sunday									

(cont. ➡)

God does have a specific plan and purpose for your life. However, what makes Christianity so different than all other religions is the fact that God wants a personal relationship with you that you freely choose to have with Him. As someone has said,

"Time is God's gift to you. How you use it is your gift to God."

As you look over your entries in your Time Alternative Choices chart, answer the following questions for each of your entries:

Entry 1

1. What did you like about the time you chose to spend with electronic media that day?

2. What did you not like about it?

3. What would you have liked about the alternate use of your time which you recorded on your chart?

4. What might you not have liked about the alternate use of your time which you recorded on your chart?

5. If you could choose how to spend your electronic media time all over again, what would you do? Please explain.

Entry 2

1. What did you like about the time you chose to spend with electronic media that day?

2. What did you not like about it?

(cont. ➥)

Name _____ Date _____

Making Sense of "Plug-In Drugs"
Part II: Reflecting on The Electronic Time Inventory: Alternate Time Choices
Week Two (Cont.)

3. What would you have liked about the alternate use of your time which you recorded on your chart?

4. What might you not have liked about the alternate use of your time which you recorded on your chart?

5. If you could choose how to spend your electronic media time all over again, what would you do? Please explain.

Name _____ Date _____

Making Sense of "Plug-In Drugs"
Part III: The Electronic Fast
Week Three (Optional)

Look at your answers to the questions at the end of Part II of this assignment. How do they make you feel about the amount of time that you spent with electronic entertainment? You may feel fine about the way you spent your time or you may not. As you look at your answers, do you feel that there might be some changes that you would like to make in how you spend your time? If so, you may consider doing the third and optional assignment of taking the "electronic fast". The electronic fast is a choice that you make not to use any electronic entertainment for an entire week. One reason to consider doing this is if you'd like to see if you feel better than you normally do at the end of the week. Another reason is if you want to make sure you do other activities with your time. If you want to take this challenge and give up all electronic entertainment for one week, then tell your teacher and sign your name on The "E" Fast form. After your fast, answer the questions below.

The "E" Fast

I, the undersigned, want to take the challenge of abstaining from all electronic entertainment for a full seven days. These are the dates of my electronic fast: From _____ to _____ .

Signed: _____ Date: _____

Your Evaluation of Your Electronic Fast

1. Did you *miss* any of the electronic entertainment that you normally use (i.e., how hard was it to do this fast?)

   If so, circle how much you missed it:

   a. lots   b. some   c. not much

(cont. ➤➤)

2. What programs, movies, or games did you miss the most? Why?

3. What activities did you do instead of electronic entertainment?

4. Which ones of these activities (from answers to #3) did you enjoy the most?

5. Which ones of these activities (from answers to #3) did you enjoy the least?

6. From doing this electronic fast, do you want to make any changes in your normal use of electronic entertainment in your daily lifestyle? Why or why not?

Name _____ Date _____

Friendships:
Understanding God's Blessings with Different Kinds of Friends

Imagine that you are walking down the street of your neighborhood one day. After you walk for a long time, you pass by a large, wealthy house with huge picture windows in the front. You don't want to look inside because you know that the people who own the house don't have a good reputation. But, you just can't resist your curiosity. As you peer through the picture windows of the house, you see that they're having a big party. You see lots of food and beverages on the table. Just before you walk by the house, someone inside catches your attention. It's your pastor! "What is my pastor doing at a party like that?" you wonder. Then you tell yourself, "No, it can't be my pastor because he would never be friends with people of such poor reputation!"

Did you know that this story was adapted from the New Testament? Yes! And, the "pastor" in the story was none other than Jesus Himself! This is how Matthew described it: "...as Jesus and His disciples were eating dinner [at Matthew the tax collector's house], there were many notorious swindlers there as guests! The Pharisees were indignant, 'Why does your teacher associate with men like that?'" (*Matthew* 9:10-11, TLB)

Have you ever seen your friends spending time with others with whom you think they "shouldn't" spend any time? You probably have. People tend to judge others by the friends they have or don't have. (This is sometimes called "guilt by association".) Why do we judge people by their friends? We do this partly because the kind of friends that a person has affects their reputation in our eyes. Everyone wants to have a good reputation—and even be popular—if they can. But, here are two good questions for you to answer:

1. Is the way that we judge others by the kind of people with whom they spend a significant amount of time always accurate? Why or why not?

2. If a Christian teenager began to wear the same kind of jeans as one of his non-Christian friends, would that automatically mean that his or her heart was being turned away from Jesus? Why or why not?

God wants you to learn how to pick good friends—whether they are Christians or non-Christians. Do you realize that you might have some "Christian" friends who are unhealthy for you to have a friendship with? This is what the apostle Paul meant when he wrote to the Christians in Corinth: "...you are not to keep company with anyone who claims to be a brother [or sister] Christian but indulges in sexual sins, or is greedy, or is a swindler, or worships idols, or is a drunkard, or abusive. Don't even eat lunch with such a person."

(*cont.* ➤➤)

(*I Corinthians* 5:11, TLB) Paul's purpose of asking Christians not to be friends with other Christians who are involved in these sins is so that these friends will repent (change their minds) and start living a holy life for Christ. He also said it so that their sin would not spread in the church—or even to your life!

Do you have any friends or associates who are *non*-Christians? I hope so, because it's okay if you do. Read what Paul wrote to the same Christians: "When I wrote to you before, I said not to mix with evil people. But, when I said that I wasn't talking about unbelievers who live in sexual sin or are greedy cheats and thieves and idol worshipers. For you can't live in this world without being with people like that." (*I Corinthians* 5:9-10, TLB) There are non-Christian friends who are healthy for you to have a friendship with *if* you know the purpose of the friendship and are in touch with your own weaknesses. Answer the following two questions:

1. What do you think a couple of reasons might be that God would like you to have some non-Christian friends?

2. Become aware of your own limitations and weaknesses. Are you strong enough to have friendships with non-Christians? Are you a positive influence upon them? Are they a negative influence upon you? E.g., we wouldn't recommend that a recovering alcoholic live next door to a bar because he knows that alcohol is a real weakness for him. What are some of your own personal areas of weakness? Why might God tell you not to have a friendship with someone in light of what your weaknesses are?

The Friendship Bridge is made up of common goals, values, ministry/help/service, and interests. There's a purpose for each friendship you have. Connect with what it is. The goal is to recognize the role (the gold/value) in each friendship that you have; to discover its unique purpose. Friendships are two-way streets—not one-way roads! Are you both spiritually, morally, emotionally, socially, or intellectually healthy for each other? Study the Friendship Bridge diagram. Read all the goals and write down which goals would make the best bridges of friendhsip using similar interests as well as someone else's need(s).

Sally or Mike's Goals

1. Physical Health
   a. To learn to play tennis
   b. To swim at public pool each month
   c. To join YWCA volleyball team
2. Mental Health
   a. To get straight "A's"
   b. To read a Christian classic
   c. To learn more about C.S. Lewis
3. Social Health
   a. To have a fun sleep-over
   b. To get to know the new neighbors
   c. To minister at the downtown mission
4. Spiritual Health
   a. To memorize 3 verses on witnessing
   b. To sit through the adult service with parent
   c. To offer to share his/her bike with new neighbor

The Friendship Bridge

Cathy or Bill's Goals

1. Physical Health
   a. To lift weights 1x/week
   b. To walk in the park with dog
   c. To ride a bike 2 mi/day
2. Mental Health
   a. To get all "B's" on report card
   b. To explore general career directions
   c. To form convictions about dating
3. Social Health
   a. To get closer to grandfather
   b. To discover some new friends
   c. To go to youth group each week
4. Spiritual Health
   a. To talk to Jesus once a day
   b. To learn to love the people I don't like
   c. To share Jesus with a neighbor at the right time

Name _____   Date _____

Evaluating Hidden Motives In Friendships

A Personal Testimony

Susan Boe

Being practically next door neighbors, it seemed natural that Tammy and I would be friends. Although we were the same age and had similar interests, our friendship had its share of ups and downs. I noticed we started to drift apart during junior high school. After not hearing from her for several months, and she not returning my phone calls, I wondered if she still wanted to be friends. When she would finally call, I would have my share of doubts as to her real motive. Did she call on a hot day just because she wanted to come over swimming in our pool, or did she really want to see me? When she called on a Saturday when she knew I normally spent time at the ranch with my horse, was it because she wanted to go riding or because she enjoyed spending time with me? This doubt about our friendship continued for years. To this day, I still do not have the confidence that Tammy really likes me for who I am.

Susan wanted to be liked and accepted just for who she was. Can you relate to her mixed feelings about her friendship with Tammy? I am sure that if Susan would have shared honestly her feelings with Tammy, she would have found that Tammy had similar feelings. Quality friendships take hard work. They require open communication and a lot of unconditional love. When making friends, both positive and negative motives can be involved.

(cont. ➥)

The following are a list of five common motives that may be influencing your friendships. Place the number for one or more of the following motivations that best describes the attitude behind the statement.

1. **Selfishness:** seeking only what you can get out of the friendship with no desire to give.

2. **Genuine acceptance:** choosing to be friends with someone just because of who they are.

3. **Fear:** acting out of a fear of rejection that you might not be accepted unless you do things to 'measure up'.

4. **Seeking approval:** choosing those who are in the "in crowd" as friends so you can belong to the most popular group.

5. **Genuine interest:** choosing a friend based upon your sincere interest in him/her as a person and having a mutual interest in one another's good.

_____ "He is so popular with others, I want to be his friend, too."

_____ "How can I benefit from being this person's friend?"

_____ "All the cool guys smoke cigarettes. I really want them to like me, so I better start smoking."

_____ "I heard the new guy in class has really rich parents; it would be great to be his friend."

_____ "She is so popular with the boys; if I were her friend, maybe the boys would like me, too."

_____ "He really seems to have his life together; what could he teach me if I got to know him?"

_____ "He is so smart, if I become his friend, maybe he would help me with my homework."

_____ "She seems to have a close relationship with God; if I got closer to her, maybe I could discover how she does it."

_____ "Our youth group leaders always ask Jan to do things with them. If I become her friend, maybe I will be recognized, too."

_____ "Steve has a lot going for him; I hope we stay friends; I want to see him reach God's full potential for his life."

_____ "I heard the new girl in class was really popular in her old school; I wonder if she will like me."

_____ "Only the people who are gifted musically get any attention in my youth group. I think I better take piano lessons."

Name _____ Date _____

Handling Conflict

Resolve each of the following conflicts effectively for a positive outcome.
(Optional: use as an in-class activity for skits or as a take-home assignment)

Situation #1

Ann and Sue argue all the time. The two sisters share a room and always have conflicts about the way the room is kept. Ann likes the room to be neat and clean, with everything in its proper place. Sue, on the other hand, is so busy with her involvements at school and gymnastics, she claims she doesn't have the time to pick up her things. Friday afternoon when the girls got home from school, Sue ran into the room, dropped her books on the floor, changed into her gymnastics uniform and left her school clothes heaped over the dresser. Ann yelled at Sue just as Sue was headed out the door to practice, "You slob! You get back in here and clean up your junk!"

How would you help Ann and Sue resolve their conflict?

Situation #2

Jared couldn't wait until his school's varsity basketball championship game Friday night. Although he played on the junior varsity team, he never missed a varsity game. He had arranged to get a ride with his best friend. They were going to go out for pizza with the team after the game. As he was leaving for school Friday morning, his mother dropped a bomb. "Jared", she said, "the babysitter is sick and can't watch your sister tonight. I have to show a house to a client. There is a pizza in the freezer and I rented some movies. I will be leaving around 6:00PM and will be back about 11:00PM." Jared erupted, "Mom, I don't want to baby-sit tonight, I have other plans. It's just not fair! And besides, you always leave me with Jesse!"

How would you help Jared and his mother overcome this conflict?

How could Jared's mother have handled this better?

Name _____ Date _____

The Power of Words
James 3

BIBLE STUDY

Death and life are in the power of the tongue.
Proverbs 18:21

When was the last time you felt that someone hurt you? Did they hurt you through what they said to you or about you? Very probably. Do you remember the last time that some-one made you feel really good? Did they do that through what they said to you or about you? Most probably. Words are very powerful! They bring life to others through encourag-ing them. But, they can also bring death to them by tearing them down in unkind ways. Read the following verses from *The Book of Proverbs*, the Bible's book of practical wisdom. This wisdom includes the best way to communicate with others so that everyone will feel understood and encouraged when we talk to them. List the one word from each verse that describes either the positive or the negative power in words.

Positive	Living Words	Negative	Deadly Words
1. *Proverbs* 10:20		1. *Proverbs* 12:19	
2. *Proverbs* 15:4		2. *Proverbs* 25:23	
3. *Proverbs* 25:25		3. *Proverbs* 28:23	
4. *Proverbs* 31:26		4. *Proverbs* 6:24	

1. Write out *Matthew* 12:34.

2. In the above verse, from where does Jesus say your words come?

3. Write out *Proverbs* 21:23.

4. From the above verse, what should you do to try to keep yourself out of trouble?

5. In what ways would guarding your words help you to keep out of trouble?

Name _____ Date _____

"Mom and Dad, Let's Talk…"

Choose the appropriate time to ask your parents the following questions. If other questions or comments come up in the discussion, please write them down. Write a brief paragraph summarizing what you learned from the discussion.

❑ What is your definition of 'single dating'?

❑ What do you think is the purpose of single dating?"

❑ What do you think about teens my age 'going together'?

❑ How would you describe my spiritual maturity level?

❑ How would you describe my emotional maturity level?

❑ Do you have a dating standard for me? If so, what is it? And why?

What have I learned from my conversation with my parent(s)?

Name _____   Date _____

Crossword

All of the following clues are represented in the crossword puzzle above. Find the correct answer to the clue and fill it in.

ACROSS

1. A very contagious condition caused by a bacterial infection

3. To chew thoroughly

7. An oily substance that can clog the pores of your skin

10. A hard substance that gives our nails their strength

12. The deepest layer of skin

15. A type of acne created when oil is trapped inside a pore

16. A substance that hardens on your teeth

17. A gum disease caused by a build-up of plaque and tartar on your teeth

18. Insects that can live in the hair and may appear to be dandruff

20. Surrounds the nail and is made of nonliving skin

21. A condition in which the outer layer of the scalp flakes off

22. The root of each hair is secured in a small pocket called a _____

23. The name given to the bone, tissue, and gum that support your teeth

DOWN

1. A clogged pore that has become infected; the most serious form of acne

2. The middle layer of skin

4. An infection of one of the small glands in your eyelid

5. A pocket in the tooth created when bacteria combines with sugary foods and forms an acid which then attacks the enamel

6. The outer layer of skin

8. A distortion in vision due to the irregular shape of the cornea or lens

9. A skin condition that occurs when the pores of the skin become clogged with oil

11. When a toenail pushes into the skin in the side of the toe it is said to be _____

13. A pore that is plugged with oil but is exposed to the air

14. A doctor who treats skin disorders

19. A grainy, sticky coating that is constantly forming on your teeth

(cont. ➥)

Match the Terms

Fill in the blanks for the remainder of the vocabulary words. The answers are below the sentences provided, but not all of the words from the list will be used as answers.

1. If you have difficulty seeing things far away you are said to be _____.

2. An advanced form of gum disease is _____

3. If your upper and lower teeth don't line up properly you have a _____.

4. Another name for bad breath is _____.

5. A procedure that uses braces to position the teeth correctly is called _____.

6. A difficulty in seeing things that are close is called _____.

A. malocclusion   F. acne

B. follicle   G. periodontal disease

C. orthodontics   H. nearsighted

D. farsightedness   I. plaque

E. halitosis   J. gingivitis

Name ______________________ Date ____________

The Importance of Personal Hygiene

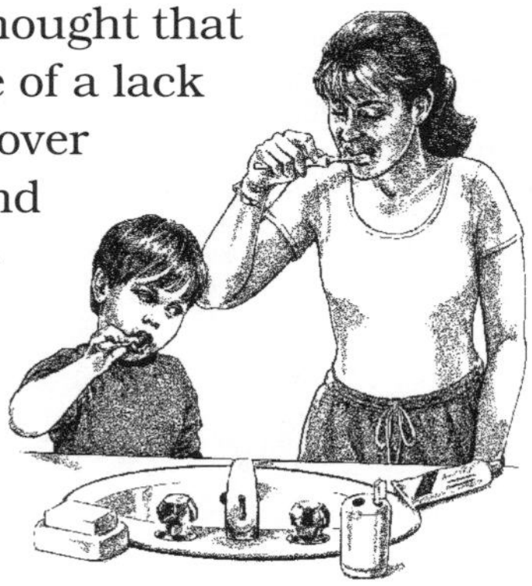

For many years, the medical profession persecuted anyone who thought that germs traveled from doctor to patient or patient to doctor because of a lack of personal hygiene. Thousands of people have needlessly died over the centuries because of the unstopped presence of bacteria and germs due to their ignorance of the extreme importance of personal hygiene to health.

1. Read *Deuteronomy* 23:12-14, "...you shall have a place outside the camp where you may go out and you shall have an implement among your equipment, and when you sit down outside, you shall dig with it and turn and cover your refuse...therefore your camp shall be holy."

   God told Moses this law of sanitation thousands of years ago so that His people might be healthy and free from sickness and disease. Verse 14 says, "...therefore your camp shall be holy." It's interesting to note that the word in the original for "holy" also includes the meaning of "healthy"! Clean hands prevent the spread of disease. List three times that a person should wash their hands with soap and warm water during the day and why.

   a. Reason:

   b. Reason:

   c. Reason:

2. Have you ever not wanted to sit next to someone in class because they "smelled so badly"? If you want to have friends, you have to keep clean and fresh. List five deodorant/anti-perspirant products. Compare the ingredients. What is the main difference in ingredients?

   a. Ingredient(s):

(cont. ➻)

b.   Ingredient(s):

c.   Ingredient(s):

d.   Ingredient(s):

e.   Ingredient(s):

What's the difference between a deodorant and an anti-perspirant?

Which do you think is necessary to use?
Why?

What causes body odor?

What do some people use as a natural alternative to these types of products?

3. List three popular mouthwashes. What is their common ingredient?
    a.   Ingredient(s):

    b.   Ingredient(s):

    c.   Ingredient(s):

What natural products are used for the same purpose?

What causes bad breath?

Name _____   Date _____

An Interview with a Dermatologist

Ask your parent(s) or friends (or look in the Yellow Pages™) for the name of a good dermatologist (skin doctor). Ask him/her the following questions either in person or over the phone, whichever is more convenient for the doctor.

1. Would you consider the skin to be the largest organ of the human body?

2. Why is the skin so important—even for a teenager? What are its functions and benefits to me?

3. What is the most common skin problem with teens my age?

4. What causes acne? Do chocolate, rest, diet, exercise, hormones, or stress play a role?

5. How do you recommend that teenagers address acne problems?

6. Tanning salons advertise providing "helio-therapy" for people. Is there such a therapeutic use of the sun?

7. What is the difference between the light from a tanning lamp and the light from the sun?

8. Can either source of light cause skin cancer? How easily? What is the process?

9. Why do people get skin cancer? What are the statistics? What ages of people does skin cancer affect the most? If I love to sunbathe a lot, could I get it, too? What could I do to prevent it? Are there any preliminary "signs" of it?

(*cont.* ➺)

10. Do sunscreens work? Which products would you recommend?

11. Would Vitamin E or olive oil help my skin? If so, where would I purchase these products and how would I use them?

12. Do "tanning" (skin-coloring or darkening) products hurt my skin in the long run? Would they discolor it?

Name _____   Date _____

Acne Products

Go to a store that has a wide selection of skin care products. Look in the acne section and fill in the following chart about acne products.

Name of Acne Product	Claim(s)	Ingredients	Directions for Use	Fragrance and/or Additives	Color and/or Additives	Cost
1.						
2.						
3.						
4.						
5.						
6.						
7.						
8.						
9.						
10.						

1. In the Ingredients column above, circle all of the ingredients that these ten products have in common. Make a note of any major differences in ingredient usage.

2. Approximately how many more different acne products were there on the shelf besides these ten? Why do you think that there are so many different acne products?

3. If any, which acne product(s) do you use? What do you like about it? What don't you like about it?

Name _____ Date _____

My Interview with My Dentist

Ask your dentist the following questions. Feel free to ask him other questions, too, as the conversation develops. (Remember that, during their workday, dentists are extremely conscious of time.)

1. Why do I have to go to the dentist every year?

2. What are your long-term goals for each of your patients?

3. Why does dentistry hurt so much? How can the pain be reduced? Are there new products coming out for this?

4. What can be done to reduce people's fears of the dentist?

5. Are there any easy ways to floss my teeth?

6. Can I get too much (overdose on) Novocaine™? Is anyone allergic to it?

7. What do you think about the use of putting someone to "sleep" in the chair? Can these gases/vapors be addictive or harmful?

8. Why do dentists make so much money? Why do so many dentists only work a four-day week?

9. What different kinds of dentists are there? If you had to do it all over again, would you choose one of these specializations?

10. Is there a lot of stress involved in dentistry? How do you handle it?

Name _____   Date _____

The Parts of the Eye

Label the parts of the eye.

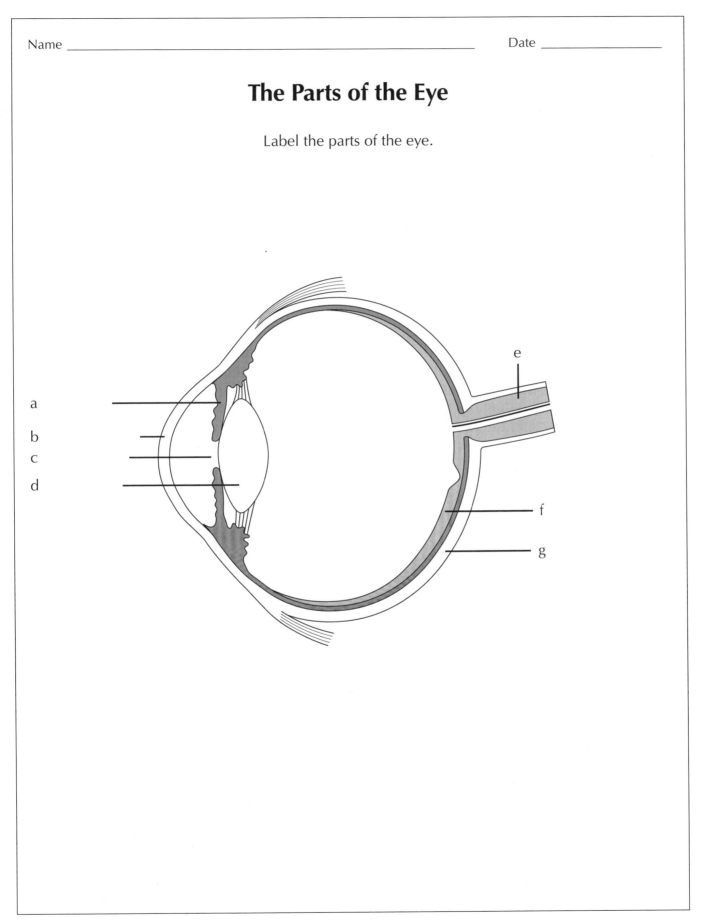

Name _____   Date _____

The Ear

Label the parts of the ear.

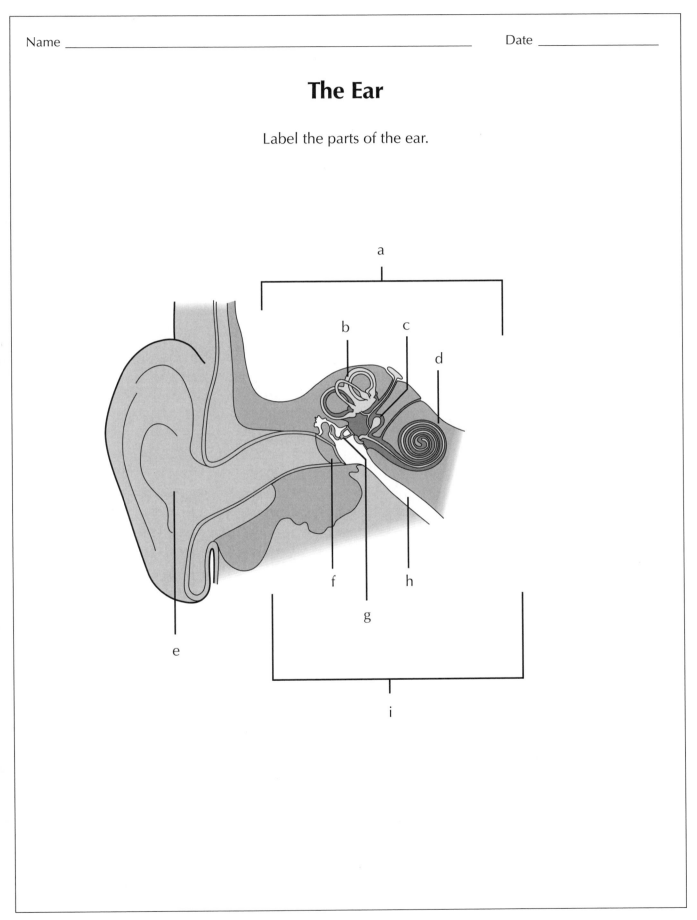

Name _____ Date _____

Crossword

All of the following clues are represented in the crossword puzzle above. Find the correct answer to the clue and fill it in.

ACROSS

3. A type of effect due to alcohol ingestion wherein the center of the brain controlling a person's shyness and self-control is blocked

7. A twelve-step group which endeavors to help the children of alcoholic parents

8. An illness characterized by excessive, habitual, and compulsive drinking

10. Substances which alter the function of one or more body processes

12. The physical disturbance that occurs when a substance to which a person is addicted is not provided to the addict

14. A resistance in the body to a substance

19. Highly addictive narcotic provided as one of the strongest types of pain killers known

20. "Angel dust" (abbreviation)

21. Refusing to acknowledge the existence of a problem

24. An extremely potent and dangerous hallucinogen (abbreviation)

25. Drugs that tend to slow down your body's nervous system

DOWN

1. A chronic liver disease often resulting from alcohol abuse

2. Use of illegal substances or misuse of legal compounds (two words)

4. Addictive compounds which may be prescribed as pain killers or cough suppressants

5. Mothers Against Drunk Driving (abbreviation)

6. A twelve step group designed to help the husbands, wives, friends and family members of both practicing and non-practicing alcoholics

8. Abbreviation for the twelve step group created to help alcoholics (abbreviation)

9. A drug that is meant to relieve pain, cure disease or prevent other illnesses

11. A common stimulant found in coffee, tea, cola, chocolate and some diet aids

13. Compounds that speed up the body's nervous system

15. A physical or mental need for a drug or other substance

16. An extremely dangerous and addictive depressant drug made from opiates

17. He discovered the drug penicillin in 1928 (last name only)

18. A form of depressant that induces sleep or suppresses feeling

22. Food and Drug Administration (abbreviation)

23. A thick, dark, and sticky liquid formed when tobacco burns

(cont. ➡)

Match the Terms

Fill in the blanks for the remainder of the vocabulary words. The answers are below the sentences provided, but not all of the words from the list will be used as answers.

1. Smoke that hangs in the air in an area where smokers have been smoking is called _____ smoke.

2. The smoke that comes from the lit end of a cigarette is referred to as _____ smoke.

3. _____ is a poisonous gas produced by automobile engines and burning tobacco, among other sources.

4. Any reaction to a drug aside from the desired one is called a _____.

5. Smoke that is inhaled and then exhaled by the smoker is _____ smoke.

6. _____ may be any of the three groupings shown in the questions above.

7. A group of drugs which cause the brain to form unreal images are the _____.

8. A highly addictive, colorless, oily, highly toxic and addictive alkaloid compound obtained from tobacco is called _____.

9. A drug sold only with a doctor's written order is a _____ drug.

10. A disease which disables the function of the alveoli (air sacs) of the lungs.

11. Drug compounds which may be purchased "over the counter" without the approval of a physician are called _____ drugs.

A. Prescription

B. Non-prescription

C. Environmental

D. Carbon monoxide

E. Hallucinogens

F. Side stream

G. Secondhand

H. Tolerance

I. Medicine

J. Side effect

K. Depressants

L. Nicotine

M. Emphysema

N. Lung cancer

O. Mainstream

P. Inhibitory

Q. Cirrhosis

Name _____   Date _____

What Does Gaining Freedom Mean to You?

Put a check mark in the box(es) of every statement below which you feel most accurately describes your definition of "freedom". Under each of the several statements below, write an evaluation of each statement as to whether you feel each statement by itself is a Biblical and adequate description of freedom or not.

❑   Freedom means doing what I want to do just as long as it is legal.
Evaluation statement:

❑   Freedom means doing what I want just as long as I don't think that it's going to hurt anyone else.
Evaluation statement:

❑   Freedom means doing whatever I want to do—just so I don't get caught.
Evaluation statement:

❑   Freedom means doing whatever my Christian friends say is okay.
Evaluation statement:

❑   Freedom is doing what my conscience allows me to do.
Evaluation statement:

❑   Freedom is doing what I want as long as it's in the privacy of my own home.
Evaluation statement:

❑   Freedom is being able to do what is right; it's having the inner desire and power inside of me to live within God's boundaries.
Evaluation statement:

Name _____ Date _____

Forming Convictions
"What Do You Believe?"
(An Interview with Significant Adults in Your Life)

Ask the following questions of a significant adult in your life whose convictions about certain areas you would be interested in knowing. Allow the discussion to branch off into other related areas, too.

1. Are you a believer? If so, how did you come to Christ?

2. What do you believe about God, Jesus Christ and the Holy Spirit?

3. Do you think that there's a real heaven? If so, who do you think goes there and when?

4. Do you think that there's a real hell? If so, who do you think goes there and when?

5. What do you think about all of the different kinds of Christian denominations? Do you think that it matters which denomination a Christian belongs to?

6. What kind of relationship to a local church do you have? Do you think that church membership makes a difference in being a Christian?

7. What do you believe about the Bible? How often do you read it? In what ways has it been a help to your Christian life?

8. Do you like to pray? What was the most exciting answer to prayer you've ever received?

(cont. ➤➤)

9. What is the most difficult part you find in sharing Jesus with others? Have you ever been afraid of being rejected?

10. What do you believe about the end of the world? Do you believe that we're living in the last generation of human history? Do you think that this makes any difference?

11. Do you think that a person's strong beliefs or convictions are important? Why or why not?

12. How many of your present convictions are the same as your parent's convictions? How many of them are different than your parent's beliefs? What do you think about this?

Name _____ Date _____

What Does the Bible Say About...

1. The existence of one God?

2. The theory of evolution?

3. The importance of having good, Christian friends?

4. A Christian dating or marrying a non-Christian?

5. Respecting and obeying one's parents?

6. Developing one's skills and talents?

7. Basing one's feelings about oneself upon other people's approval?

8. Homosexuality?

9. Social drinking? Getting drunk? Alcoholism?

10. Obeying and disobeying the government?

11. Who Jesus Christ is?

12. The place of the local church in the life of a Christian?

13. How to share one's faith with non-believers?

14. The place of giving money to God's work?

15. If there's a sin too great for God to forgive?

Name _____ Date _____

God, My Father
A Study on the Fatherhood of God

Answer the following questions about God as your heavenly Father.

1. Look up the word "father" in a Bible concordance. List four ways—with the verses—that Jesus used the term "Father" when He talked about God in the *Gospel of John*. Which term of "Father" did He use the most?

    a.

    b.

    c.

    d.

2. Does the New Testament teach that God is the Father of everyone—both believers and non-believers—or just of believers? If God is not exactly the "father" of non-believers, what would He be considered in relationship to them?

3. What three things do you think that a good father should do for his family?

    a.

    b.

    c.

4. Do you see God doing these things for you as your heavenly Father?

5. How does someone become a child of God, and, thereby, know God as one's heavenly Father? If you don't know Him as your Father in this way as yet, would you like to?

(cont. ➥*)*

6. When you talk to God, by what do you address Him the most? God? Jesus? Father? Lord? When you call God your Father, how does it make you feel?

7. List two men whom you think are good fathers. Explain why you think that they are good fathers.

   a.   Reason:

   b.   Reason:

8. What is the most meaningful part of God being your heavenly Father?

Name _____ Date _____

Your Life Goals

Whether you think you know what God has called you to do as a career and/or ministry or not, God will still guide you as you ask Him. Answer the following questions concerning your goals and desires for the future.

1. Make a list of your personal goals and/or desires for the following time frames.

   "In one year, I see myself…"

   "In five years, I see myself…"

   "In ten years, I see myself…"

2. In all of your planning for the future, what have you probably failed to take into consideration?

(*cont.* ➡)

3. Do you think that the use of drugs might interfere with your future life goals? Why or why not. Please explain.

4. Write out the following verses. Apply them to your own life in a brief paragraph.

   • *Jeremiah* 29:11

   Verse:

   Application:

   • *II Corinthians* 5:17

   Verse:

   Application:

   • *Matthew* 6:33

   Verse:

   Application:

Name _____ Date _____

Vocabulary

Each of the six terms below has been used both correctly and incorrectly in a sentence. Select the line that best describes in context the definition of the term and circle the letter at the start of that sentence. Circle either "A" or "B" for each choice.

Comprehension   Regress   Hypocrite   Intellectual   Humility   Countenance

A. Susan was able to explain what she had read and so was certain her **comprehension** of the material was adequate.

B. Stan enjoyed the book but felt that the **comprehension** was dry and poorly presented.

A. I decided to attempt to **regress** those topics in my speech to the class.

B. After seeing his patient make so much progress, it bothered Dr. Stanton to see his condition **regress**.

A. Stephen wanted to appear that he understood his topic and hoped the audience would see him as a **hypocrite**.

B. She knew that by saying one thing and doing the opposite, she would probably be perceived as a **hypocrite**.

A. Catrina thoroughly researched and understood her subject and so appeared to have the more **intellectual** of the two presentations.

B. My **intellectual** condition was good but my mind was in a shambles.

A. He was so embarrassed, he finally felt he understood the meaning of **humility**.

B. Tiffany realized the project was a big one and had the **humility** to ask for help.

A. It was clear from her **countenance** that she was feeling pure joy at that moment.

B. The numbers all added up correctly, so his **countenance** must have been correct.

Name _____   Date _____

Questions: The Road to Invention and Discovery

List five famous people from the textbook. Write the question they may have asked that may have helped lead them to their major discovery or invention.

Name	Question(s)	Discovery/Invention

List three questions that might motivate you to want to create an invention or make a discovery someday.

1.

2.

3.

Name _____   Date _____

What Were You Thinking!?

Read the following situations. In the space provided, write what you think each was thinking as they made their choices, what the consequences might be, then explain what you would have done in the same situation and why.

Situation	What were they thinking?	What was the consequence?	What would you have done?
1. After ruining her sister's CD player, Ann blamed it on her younger brother, Timmy. Timmy got punished; Ann got away with it...except Timmy never forgot.			
2. Steven was not to trade his basketball cards with friends without his parents' permission. But, he did it anyway. When his parents noticed that one of the more expensive cards had disappeared, Steven told them he lost it. But, his little brother spilled the beans. His parents grounded him for a double length of time for lying as well as disobeying.			
3. Joe stood by and watched while some of his friends vandalized the school one evening. The police arrived and took them all to the station, where Joe's parents had to bail him out.			
4. Sara spent the night at a friend's house. With the parents asleep, they snuck out of the house and went to a party. When Sara awoke the next morning, she could not remember many of the things that her friends were telling her that she had done at the party. After vomiting all morning, Sara went home and told her Mom she had the stomach flu.			

Name _____   Date _____

Growing in Wisdom

So when they [Joseph and Mary] had performed all things according to the law of the Lord, they returned to Galilee, to their own city, Nazareth. And the Child [Jesus] grew and became strong in spirit, filled with wisdom; and the grace of God was upon Him…And Jesus increased in wisdom and stature and in favor with God and men.
Luke 2:39, 40, 52

1. Look up in a Bible and/or an English dictionary, three definitions of the word "wise" or "wisdom" and record them here.

   a.

   b.

   c.

2. In Scripture, foolishness is the opposite of wisdom. Look up in a Bible and/or an English dictionary, three definitions of the word "foolishness" or "foolish" and record them here.

   a.

   b.

   c.

3. Find three verses in the *Book of Proverbs*, the Bible's book of useful wisdom, that clearly state what is practical wisdom for a person to do. Do this by looking up the words "wise" and "wisdom" in a Bible concordance.

   a.

   b.

   c.

4. Find three verses in the *Book of Proverbs*, the Bible's book of useful wisdom, that clearly state what is practical foolishness for a person to do. Do this by looking up the words "fool", "foolish", and "foolishness" in a Bible concordance.

   a.

(cont. ➥)

b.

c.

5. Learn how to apply wisdom to real-life situations. Complete the following situation statements with what you think would be the wisest choice(s) for a Christian teen to make:

a. When a good-looking, non-Christian guy asks a Christian girl out on a date whom she has known all her life, I think the wisest action for her to take would be to...

b. When there's going to be an R-rated movie playing at Gary's party that Steve is going to, I think the wisest action for Steve to take would be to...

c. When Eddy's older brother, who's a straight "A" student in college, asks his younger brother, Jerry, if he wants to watch him smoke a little pot and look at a *Playboy* magazine, I think the wisest action for Jerry to take would be to...

6. Look up the phrase "blind spot" in an English dictionary or talk to a trusted adult as to the meaning of the phrase and record it here. (Record the meaning that applies to people's character rather than to the retina of the eye.) What is the one main area in life in which you feel you may have a "blind spot"; the area of weakness in your life for which you need the most wisdom? How might you provide more wisdom for yourself in that area?

a. Definition of a blind spot:

b. One of your personal blind spots:

c. How you're going to get more wisdom for this blind spot:

Name _____   Date _____

Vocabulary

Prayer describes our communication with God. Write a paragraph describing either the importance of prayer in your own relationship with God or an example of when prayer was of special meaning to you in dealing with a situation in your life.

Fear is a concern or anxiety about something real or imagined. Describe how a close walk with God helps to alleviate or neutralize fear in the life of a believer or share a personal story from your own experience in which your reliance on God's strength calmed your fear.

Destiny is the unique purpose for which God has created each one of us. What things do you think would be helpful in coming to fully understand God's plan for your life? What are you doing now to realize His will for you?

Name _____   Date _____

The Importance of Prayer

1. Look up the words "pray" and "prayer" in a Bible dictionary and/or an English dictionary. Record three definitions here.

   a.

   b.

   c.

2. Read all of *Matthew* 7:7-11. Verse 11 says, "If you then, being evil, know how to give good gifts to your children, how much more will your Father who is in heaven give good things to those who ask Him." From these verses, what can you learn about the attitude of the Father toward His children?

   How could this give you confidence in your prayers?

3. Read all of *Luke* 11:5-10. Verse 10 says, "For everyone who asks [keeps on asking] receives, and he who seeks [keeps on seeking] finds, and to him who knocks [keeps on knocking], it will be opened." To what kind of prayer does God respond?

4. Read all of *Luke* 18:10-14. Verse 14 says, "...for everyone who exalts himself will be abased and he who humbles himself will be exalted." From this story, what two character qualities are required for God to answer prayer?

   a.

   b.

5. Read *Matthew* 5:20-24. Verse 24 says, "First be reconciled to your brother, and then come and offer your gift." What kind of attitude toward others does God require for us to have before He will hear our prayers?

(cont. ➥)

6. Read *Luke* 5:16, "So He Himself [Jesus] often withdrew into the wilderness and prayed." Why do you think that Jesus often withdrew from the people and His busy ministry schedule in order to pray? What might this teach you about your conversations with God?

7. Explain how the following verses teach us more about how to get our prayers answered:

   • Simplicity and sincerity, *Matthew* 6:5

   • Faith, *Mark* 9:23

Name _____ Date _____

"So, What's the Big Deal?"
A Study on Hypocrisy

1. Look up "hypocrisy" in a dictionary. What is its definition?

2. A person who practices hypocrisy is called _____.

3. Look up the word "deceive" in a dictionary. What is its definition?

4. How is hypocrisy like deceit?

5. Look in a thesaurus and list three other words used for hypocrite or hypocrisy.

6. Look up the following references. Write down the instance of hypocrisy, who the hypocrite(s) was, and the reason Jesus criticized them.

    *   *Matthew* 26:25

        a. Instance:

        b. Hypocrite(s):

        c. Reason:

    *   *Matthew* 15:1-9

        a. Instance:

        b. Hypocrite(s):

        c. Reason:

(cont. ➼)

- *Matthew* 22:18
    a. Instance:
    b. Hypocrite(s):
    c. Reason:

- *John* 8:1-11
    a. Instance:
    b. Hypocrite(s):
    c. Reason:

- *Luke* 13:10-17
    a. Instance:
    b. Hypocrite(s):
    c. Reason:

7. Write out *James* 3:17.

Name _____ Date _____

An Honest Evaluation

How do you wish your spiritual life was different? In the space provided, write what your present actions are in regard to each topic. Then write how you hope to improve.

MY CHOICE OF FRIENDS

My present situation:

How I am going to improve:

MY READING OF THE WORD

My present situation:

How I am going to improve:

MY PRAYER LIFE

My present situation:

How I am going to improve:

MY DESIRE TO SERVE GOD

My present situation:

How I am going to improve:

Name _____   Date _____

A Letter to God

Do you ever find yourself spending hours on a phone talking to your best friend, or writing lengthy letters or email to a friend who may live far away? Just as you would share with your best friend, God wants to hear all about your daily activities—both the good and the bad. He already knows all about your life, but He wants to hear from you, personally. Nothing is insignificant, stupid, or a waste of His time.

Write a letter to Jesus, expressing your thoughts as you would to a best friend. You do not have to share this with others—this is just between you and God.

Choose from the following subjects (whatever relates to you right now). On a separate piece of paper, write a letter to God as if He were your best friend and share with Him your thoughts and feelings. If you feel it would help you, use one of the following lines as a start.

- Lord, I need your strength to handle all the pressure I'm feeling…

- Lord, I had an awful day (week, month) and I need to tell you about it…

- Lord, I am struggling with my parents and family and I need your help…

- Lord, I am really having a hard time in school; can you help me?

- Lord, I really like this guy/girl and he/she is always on my mind; please help me focus on what I need to do…

- Lord, there are so many people suffering in this world; why do you let this happen, and how can I help?

- Lord, I am so happy right now and want to thank you for all the blessings in my life…

- Lord, I don't feel like I know you personally, and I would like a relationship with you; please help me…

- Lord, I have made a terrible mistake; please forgive me and help me be strong…

After writing my letter to God, I felt…

Student Text Chapter Reviews

(These are the Chapter Reviews that occur at the end of each chapter in the student text.)

Name _____ Date _____

Defining the Terms (use the Glossary if necessary)

Temptation:

Consequences:

Influences:

Habits:

Deception:

Soul:

Total Health:

Recalling the Facts

1. What caused Eve to begin to question God's laws of the Garden?

2. How did Adam and Eve's decision to eat the apple immediately affect their relationship with God?

3. Explain what is meant by the phrase "forbidden fruit".

4. Compare the Tree of Life with the Tree of Death as it relates to your relationships with others.

5. When Adam and Eve ate from the forbidden tree, and hid from God, how did God respond to them?

6. How has Eve's decision affected all of mankind today? Give one example under each of the following categories: physically, mentally, socially, and spiritually.

Applying the Truth

1. Eve allowed Satan to entice her with his deceptive words and by the sight of the delicious looking fruit (Genesis 3:1-6). Read Proverbs 1:15; 3:7. Discuss how Solomon advised people to handle evil influences. How might this truth apply to your daily life?

2. What painful struggles might the "forbidden fruit" represent to you and many other young teenagers?

3. Evaluate yourself for a moment. Do you face your battles alone, or do you talk to someone else about them? Who would be your first choice to talk to and why would you choose him/her? What makes him/her a positive or negative choice?

4. What choices do you face today that may positively or negatively influence your future?

Name _____   Date _____

Defining the Terms

Healthy:

Cells:

Tissues:

Organ:

Arteries:

Veins:

Capillaries:

Plasma:

Red blood cells:

White blood cells:

Platelets:

Arteriosclerosis:

Blood pressure:

Stroke:

Pharynx:

Trachea:

Esophagus:

Epiglottis:

Lungs:

Diaphragm:

Skeletal muscle:

Smooth muscle:

Cardiac muscle:

Digestion:

Alimentary canal:

Large intestine:

Small intestine:

Kidneys:

Hormones:

Pituitary gland:

Thyroid gland:

Adrenal glands:

Homeostasis:

Ovaries:

Testes:

Recalling the Facts

1. Explain the common characteristics of every single cell.

2. List the four primary types of tissues in the body and explain their general function.

3. Explain how the circulatory system is like a "roadway" network in your body. Include in your answer its four main functions.

4. Explain how the act of breathing is both voluntary and involuntary.

Name _____ Date _____

(continued)

5. What are the four main functions of the skeletal system?

6. Explain what is meant by the phrase: "For every action there is an equal and opposite reaction of a muscle". Give one example of this principle.

7. Explain how the excretory system is like the exhaust system of a car.

Applying the Truth

1. What body systems are helped by consistent physical activity? How does exercise help them?

2. Which body systems are hurt by the poor eating habits a person might have? How does a poor diet hurt these systems? Give an example of how you might change your personal diet to help these systems of your body.

3. After reading this chapter, list four facts or observations about your body that show how awesome of a creation it is.

Name _____ Date _____

Defining the Terms

Balanced diet:

Calorie:

Empty calories:

Nutrients:

Proteins:

Essential amino acids:

Vegetarian diet:

Carbohydrates:

Fats:

Saturated fat:

Cholesterol:

Unsaturated fats:

Vitamins:

RDA:

Water-soluble:

Fat-soluble:

Minerals:

Metabolic rate:

Diet:

Overweight:

Obese:

Anorexia:

Bulimia:

Chronic overeating:

Recalling the Facts

1. What are the guidelines on the Daily Food Pyramid? Include a possible adjustment to the Pyramid recommendations that might be even healthier.

2. Explain the difference between saturated fats and unsaturated fats. Which are more dangerous for your body and why? Give one food example for each.

3. Explain why your body needs an adequate amount of water each day. Include in your answer six ways your body uses water.

4. What is the main purpose of keeping a food journal?

5. What are four better ways of making food choices in your life?

6. What are the dangers of "fad" diets? Why do "diets" make you think only of the short-term?

Applying the Truth

1. Explain how a pizza could be a potentially healthy meal. With this in mind, describe what kind of "healthy" pizza you would order.

2. Choose three "keys to a great food journal". Explain why each might be difficult to do.

Name _____   Date _____

(continued)

3. What in the Food Guide Pyramid surprised you? How might following the Food Guide Pyramid be different than your food choices you are making now?

4. Explain one reason why package labels can be misleading to consumers.

5. Imagine that you have a friend about whose poor eating habits you are very concerned. How might you determine if they have a problem with anorexia or bulimia? What might you say and/or do to help your friend?

Name _____   Date _____

Defining the Terms

Fitness:

Cardiovascular fitness:

Atrophy:

Aerobic:

Anaerobic:

Muscular fitness:

Flexibility:

Body composition:

Lifetime sport(s):

Recalling the Facts

1. List ten benefits of exercise.

2. Explain why the most important measurement of your fitness is cardiovascular fitness.

3. Explain the difference between aerobic and anaerobic exercise and give one example of each kind of activity. Why are they both important?

4. Why is the phrase, "No pain, No gain" incorrect when it comes to stretching and exercise?

5. Explain the importance of a good warm-up and warm-down when exercising.

Applying the Truth

1. What is the important role that exercise has in controlling one's weight? How might you include more activity in your lifestyle?

2. What is meant by the phrase, "accidental workout"? Include in your answer any accidental workouts that your personal lifestyle already includes.

3. Many teenagers compare themselves with others. How can comparison be dangerous, and what does God think about it?

Name _____ Date _____

Defining the Terms

Disease:

Infectious disease:

Noninfectious disease:

Germ(s) or pathogen(s):

Symptom(s):

Viruses:

Bacteria:

Resident bacteria:

Antibodies:

Lymphocytes:

Vaccine:

STDs:

Convictions:

AIDS:

HIV:

Cancer:

Tumors:

Carcinogen:

Congenital:

Insulin:

Hypoglycemia:

Diabetes type I:

Diabetes type II:

Recalling the Facts

1. Why is homeostasis so important for your body?

2. Explain the infectious disease process.

3. How might you explain to a friend that the human body has both good and bad bacteria? Why are good bacteria considered as "friendly" bacteria?

4. How are most germs carried and passed on to another human being? What can a person do to help decrease the spread of germs?

5. Explain how God has designed your body with its own physical defenses to fight off sickness.

6. What is the only way to prevent getting a sexually transmitted disease?

7. What factors increase your chance of developing cancer? Which of these factors do you believe you can directly control?

8. How can you begin at a young age to prevent heart disease?

Name _____ Date _____

(continued)

Applying the Truth

1. What can you learn from Kristen's attitude about life (story section 5.1)? How might her story relate to James 1:17, "Every good gift and every perfect gift is from above and comes down from the Father of lights..."?

2. What is meant by the phrase "Listen to your body"?

3. What other defenses do you have as a Christian to fight off disease and sickness?

4. As you evaluate your present lifestyle, what aspects could you change to help you prevent disease as you get older?

5. Why is it important to develop strong convictions about your personal sexual boundaries before you find yourself in a relationship with the opposite sex?

Name _____ Date _____

Defining the Terms

Mature:

Confident:

Personal identity:

Jealousy:

Pride:

Character:

Self-esteem:

Recalling the Facts

1. List some of the physical, mental (emotional), social, and spiritual changes that take place in a teen's life.

2. Why do teens usually experience certain feelings, like frustration and disappointment, more intensely than adults?

3. Explain how you can begin to replace feelings of worry with feelings of faith and trust in God.

4. What is one of the main purposes behind the changes in your life?

Applying the Truth

1. Read Jeremiah 18:3-4 about the potter and the clay. Describe the process required to create a beautiful vessel. Apply this truth to the changes taking place in your own life.

2. If a very angry friend asked you, "If God really loves me, why did He let my parents split up?", what would you say to your friend?

3. Why does God warn us against comparison and jealousy?

4. Choose one of the following biblical illustrations and write an essay explaining what principle(s) of life can be learned from their example: The Faithful Servant (Luke 16:10), Samuel (I Samuel 16:7), King David (Psalms 22:1, 124:7), Judas (Matthew 26:14-16), Joseph (Genesis 37:4, 39:20, 40:23), and Peter (Mark 14:66-72; Acts 3:11-26).

Name _____ Date _____

Defining the Terms

Distract:

Self-control:

Boundary:

Goal(s):

Short-term goal:

Long-term goal:

Recalling the Facts

1. What kind of message(s) do you get from society about success? How does this message differ from what God thinks about success?

2. List the seven steps to success.

3. How are you to make wise decisions that please God and bring success?

Applying the Truth

1. It's not very difficult to become mentally focused on activities that you enjoy, but it's often difficult to focus on those that you don't really enjoy. Name three areas in your life where you believe you could become more focused. Explain what personal changes you could make in each area to help you stay focused.

2. What are boundaries? Why are they important in your life?

3. How would you describe the difference between a sin and a mistake?

4. When you sin, how do you think Satan wants you to feel? How does this differ from the way God wants you to feel?

Name _____ Date _____

Defining the Terms

Social health:

Friendship:

Relationship:

Substitutions:

Artificial relationships:

Communication:

Verbal communication:

Nonverbal communication:

Walls (between people):

Infatuation:

Positive peer pressure:

Negative peer pressure:

Respect:

Disrespect:

Reputation:

Revenge:

Forgive(ness):

Empathy:

Recalling the Facts

1. What's the danger in substituting a "thing" for a real person—maybe even a friend-ship? Give two examples of "things" that can be replacements for friendships.

2. What's the most famous "best friend" relationship in the Bible? What made their friendship so unique?

3. What's meant by the phrase, "Most people can *talk*, but not everyone can genuinely *communicate*"?

4. List the twelve skills of good communication.

5. List the keys to consider before you get emotionally involved with someone of the opposite sex.

6. How can a person avoid negative peer pressure?

Applying the Truth

1. Read Matthew 12:33-37. Explain how this passage can relate to the everyday life of a teenager.

Name _____ Date _____

(continued)

2. The Bible condemns partiality. Read James 2:1-13 and explain how this principle can be applied to your life.

3. Read Proverbs 11:13. Do you find yourself talking behind someone's back or speaking negatively about others? If you do, you may develop the reputation of being a gossip. Why don't those who gossip have many friends? What can a person do to help themselves overcome the temptation to gossip?

Name _____ Date _____

Defining the Terms

Epidermis:

Dermis:

Subcutaneous layer:

Acne:

Sebum:

Whitehead:

Blackhead:

Pimple:

Dermatologist:

Follicle(s):

Dandruff:

Head lice:

Keratin:

Cuticle:

Ingrown toenail:

Masticate:

Periodontium:

Cavity:

Plaque:

Tartar:

Gingivitis:

Periodontal disease:

Malocclusion:

Orthodontics:

Halitosis:

Farsightedness:

Nearsightedness:

Astigmatism:

Pink eye:

Sty:

Recalling the Facts

1. Why should you take the time to develop good habits of personal hygiene?

2. What is the worst time for your skin to be exposed to the sun during the day? Why?

3. If you get acne, what are five Do's and three Don'ts of caring for your skin?

4. What are the three factors to keep in mind when your hair doesn't seem to cooperate with what you're trying to do, or you just feel it's time for a style change?

Name _____ Date _____

(continued)

5. List the ways to take good care of your teeth.

6. What part of the eye is responsible for controlling the amount of light that enters the eye?

7. What is the most common form of ear trouble?

8. How might a person do a "posture check" on him/herself?

9. What might you tell a friend who wants to stop biting his/her fingernails?

Applying the Truth

1. *The lamp of the body is the eye. If therefore your eye is good,*
   your whole body will be full of light.
   Matthew 6:22

   The Bible uses the natural illustration of the eye to illustrate a spiritual truth. What did Jesus mean when He described your eye as the "lamp" of your body? How might this spiritual truth relate specifically to a teenager like yourself?

2. Read James 1;19-20. Why do you think the Bible addresses the issue of anger? What might listening and speaking have to do with getting angry?

3. Read Proverbs 20:12. God has made both your eyes and ears. How do you think that you can use your eyes and ears the most to please God?

Name _____   Date _____

Defining the Terms

Cirrhosis:

Inhibitory effect:

Alcoholism:

Tolerance level:

Withdrawal:

MADD:

Alcoholics Anonymous (AA):

Alateen:

Al-Anon:

Alexander Fleming:

Drugs:

Medicine(s):

Drug abuse:

Prescription drug:

Nonprescription drug:

FDA:

Side effects:

Caffeine:

Stimulants:

Addiction:

Depressants:

Narcotics:

Morphine, codeine:

Heroin:

Hallucinogen:

PCP or angel dust (phencyclidine):

LSD (lysergic acid diethylamide):

Denial:

Nicotine:

Tar:

Carbon monoxide:

Emphysema:

Second-hand smoke:

Mainstream smoke:

Sidestream smoke:

Environmental smoke:

Recalling the Facts

1. What is God's "Freedom Formula"?

2. How can teens' increasing sense of personal freedom contribute to their desire to try dangerous substances?

3. List five immediate effects of alcohol on the body when a person drinks too much.

Name _____ Date _____

(continued)

4. Explain the meaning of the phrase, "Advertisers don't care about your health, they only care about your money!"

5. Explain how coffee, tea, and certain soda pop, can be considered drugs. What are some of the withdrawal symptoms people might experience when going without these products?

6. List five of the nine negative effects of using marijuana.

7. Explain the importance of not trying a drug, like marijuana, not even once.

8. Why do you think young teens still smoke even though they know it's dangerous?

Applying the Truth

1. What is meant by the phrase, "You must 'own' your own faith"?

2. Give four examples of how the Bible gives you practical advice for today. List the verses.

3. How can teenagers experience part of the "kingdom of heaven" right now in their own lives?

Name _____ Date _____

Defining the Terms

Comprehension:

Intellectual:

Regress:

Humility:

Hypocrites:

Countenance:

Recalling the Facts

1. What famous church leaders may have asked the following questions:

   • Doesn't the Bible say that we are saved by faith and not by works?

   • How does the biblical doctrine of God's sovereignty apply to our daily lives?

   • Why can't I translate the Bible into the language of the common man?

   • How can true revival be maintained?

   • What kind of method can we use to teach Christians to be holy and disciplined?

2. One of the foundations to all of your leadership skills is your reading and comprehension. List five things you can do in order to increase your reading skills.

3. If asking questions is good, when does it become wrong or bad?

4. List five ways to show respect to your parents (or anyone!).

5. What does it mean to allow your parents to "save face"? Why is this a sign of respect?

Applying the Truth

1. After reading this chapter on questions, think of five sincere questions you have for God and write them on a piece of paper. The next time you're alone with God in prayer, share with Him one or two of these concerns. Keep an open mind and heart as you listen for Him to speak to you. He may not answer right away, and His response may not be the answer you were hoping for, but He will meet with you if you seek Him sincerely.

2. Set up alone time with your Dad or Mom. Ask him/her two of the questions on page 280. As they begin sharing with you, also ask them two of your own questions. Evaluate the quality time you shared, and see how you can improve your communication.

Name _____   Date _____

Defining the Terms

Prayer:

Fear:

Destiny:

Recalling the Facts

1. What factors influence your view of God?

2. What are two main goals of Bible reading?

3. What does it mean to "abide" in God throughout the day?

4. How is your life like a puzzle?

Applying the Truth

1. I Corinthians 15:33 says: "Do not be deceived. 'Evil company corrupts good habits'." How might this verse apply to your own life?

2. The Bible says that Satan is the "father of lies"(Read John 8:44). How might knowing this help you to recognize his schemes against you? Apply James 4:7 to your life: "Submit to God. Resist the devil and he will flee from you".

3. What does it mean for a teenager to "count the cost" of being a Christian? What does it mean to "fake" your Christianity? Why might teens act this way? How do you think this makes God feel?

4. You can learn to hear God's voice—personally. How might God speak to you?